Implementing a Broadband LAN

Brian Hudson and Bill Taylor

PUBLISHED BY NCC PUBLICATIONS

British Library Cataloguing in Publication Data

Hudson, Brian
  Implementing a broadband LAN
  1. Local area networks (computer networks)
  I. Title   II. Taylor, Bill
  004.6'8   TK5105.7

  ISBN 0-85012-500-6

First published in 1986 by:

NCC Publications, The National Computing Centre Limited, Oxford Road, Manchester M1 7ED, England.

Typeset in 11pt Times Roman by H & H Graphics, 2 Duke Street, Blackburn; and printed by Hobbs the Printers of Southampton.

ISBN 0-85012-500-6

Acknowledgements

The authors wish to thank the following organisations for their literature and invaluable help in the preparation of this book:

Anixter Communications (UK) Ltd
Ferranti Computer Systems
Information Technology Ltd
3M (UK) Ltd

The authors are deeply indebted to the following individuals for their advice and comments on the text:

Simon Fox, Information Technology Ltd
Malachy Smith, Intelligence (IRL) Ltd
Tony Sweeney, Ferranti Computer Systems
Don Wilkin, 3M (UK) Ltd
Kirk Gee
Colin Pye   } National Computing Centre
Geoff Simons

Special thanks to Ambrose Glackin.

The Centre acknowledges with thanks the support provided by the Electronics and Avionics Requirements Board of the Department of Industry for the project from which this publication derives.

Introduction

GENERAL

This book is intended to assist those in a wide variety of organisations who are seeking a comprehensive means of satisfying their local communication requirements and who are considering the use of a broadband local area network.

In a given situation, the selection of the most appropriate LAN product must necessarily follow from a detailed analysis of the requirements which must be satisfied. This may or may not indicate that a broadband solution is the most effective.

In this book particular attention is focused on broadband for several related reasons. Firstly, as the next chapter shows, broadband technology currently offers the only practical means of achieving the service and function integration which is the inevitable strategy for the future. Secondly, the controversy which has surrounded baseband and broadband as competing rather than complementary technologies has left a legacy of confusion among some potential users: it is important that broadband is correctly placed in the overall context of LAN provision. Finally, broadband technology is analogue and therefore tends to be unfamiliar to those whose background is predominantly that of computers and digital communication.

There is a shortage of skilled manpower capable of designing and implementing broadband networks. From the individual organisation's point of view this is an important factor. It is necessary to decide at an early stage whether in-house expertise exists or is worth acquiring, or whether reliance is to be placed entirely on the vendor or external consultant.

In the following chapters, sufficient information is presented to enable those concerned to assess both their likely commitment to networking and their existing expertise, as well as deciding on the appropriateness of a broadband solution. Other chapters consider steps in the implementation process which are less technology-dependent but which nonetheless are essential. These include the establishment of networking requirements, the installation process, and system procurement.

BACKGROUND KNOWLEDGE

It is expected that most readers will be familiar with the principles of a local area network but may have less understanding of the concepts employed in a broadband network.

In essence, broadband networks use radio-frequency techniques in the transmission of analogue or digital data over a coaxial cable network.

This method of providing a data communications network has been around since the late nineteen-sixties and is based on cable television technology, otherwise known as Community Antennae Television (CATV).

Much of the hardware orginally developed for CATV – such as the coaxial cable, RF (radio frequency) modems, taps and amplifiers – has been exploited for use in a broadband data network.

The simplest configuration of a broadband network is one where each data signal is allocated a unique frequency channel on the cable, enabling (as with television programmes) several data signals to co-exist simultaneously on the network.

Broadband's unique multiple channel ability, where a single cable is able to support hundreds of unique analogue or digital signals, provides the network with a versatile transmission medium on which to base a local area network.

Appendix 1 reviews the principles of broadband LANs in more detail.

Contents

1 Local Communications

BACKGROUND

The development of computer technology during the last decade has led to a dramatic fall in the cost of processing power and the availability of a wide range of comparatively low-cost equipment, most notably the personal computer.

Mainframe computers are of course well-established, and in the past local communication requirements for terminals have been met by dedicated (point-to-point) links, or by some form of switched network such as the internal telephone system. As the use of specialist minicomputers and more particularly personal computing facilities has grown however, it has become clear that these solutions are inadequate. If maximum benefit is to be obtained by using computer-based equipment, a high level of integration is needed. It must be possible to transfer information rapidly and easily between a wide range of terminals and hosts, and easy access must be provided to common resources such as databases. In addition, other resources such as letter quality printers or hard disk storage are both too expensive and impractical to provide them on an individual basis and they need to be shared effectively between a community of users.

Paralleling the development in computer technology therefore has been the growth in local communications and in particular that of the local area network (LAN).

For some applications, for example office systems, information and resource sharing are the principal justifications of a LAN, but other advantages emerge when the general characteristics of conventional communication networks are considered. In the past, different technologies were developed to deal with different types of information and so it is usual to find separate networks handling, for example, speech, data and video. Responsibility for the operation and maintenance of these networks will often be divided within an organisation and this makes it difficult to provide cost-effective day-to-day operation. More significantly perhaps, it can easily hamper the establishment and effective operation of a coherent corporate communications policy.

Conventional networks may have a severely restricted data speed (as low as 600 bits per second) which make them totally unsuitable for the new types of data traffic such as file transfers, and it is not uncommon to find that there is an unacceptably high error rate (perhaps as high as 1 in 10^4) which further reduces the network throughput.

Flexibility is an additional characteristic which is essential for a modern communications network. Flexibility is important because most organisations are not static, and relatively frequent relocations of staff and their equipment (including, in the future, workstations) are necessary. A related factor is that users within the organisation will expect the network to expand to meet the increased communications demand as new technologies are absorbed. The structure of conventional networks makes it time consuming and costly to modify the network when equipment is relocated or when new equipment is added, because this invariably involves the installation of new cabling. These operations frequently lead to a reduced level of reliability and, as many organisations are discovering, a situation in which spare cable ducting is rapidly becoming exhausted.

Perhaps one of the most important problems is the variety of equipment for which the direct exchange of information is difficult or impossible, and for which conventional networks offer no solution.

LOCAL AREA NETWORKS

The most significant development in recent years which has attempted to solve these problems has been the local area network. In principle, this consists of a single cable system which is run throughout the service area and to which all devices are connected. This allows each item of equipment on the network to be connected to any other item although not necessarily to communicate with it; inter-communication will depend on whether the individual protocols are compatible and on any additional features which the network may offer, such as protocol conversion. Equipment is connected to the network via network interface units, and new devices can be added or existing equipment relocated easily either by a plug and socket arrangement or by some other means which involves cutting the cable to accept a new interface unit. For most users, one of the important attractions of a LAN will be that new cabling will only need to be installed to expand the network service area.

To ensure that a reasonably large community of users can be accommodated, the cable has a large bandwidth (ie high data rate) and access is normally on an equal priority basis. Local area networks need to be distinguished from other types of networks but a precise definition has proved difficult to formulate (see Reference 1.1). This is not perhaps surprising because the nature of networks makes the abrupt divisions needed for a definition artificial, and it is generally more useful to consider instead the distinguishing features of a LAN. The principal features are:

— it is a network which serves a limited geographical area such as a building, a campus or a factory computer. Typically the distances involved are up to a kilometre but can extend to 10 km;

— it is owned and operated by the user organisation and the public telecommunications authority is not normally involved;

— users receive all data transmitted over the network and select only that addressed to them;

— all users have an equal opportunity to gain access to the network;

— there is no constraint on the technology that can be used, and its selection is determined by the user organisation's requirements;

— the data error rate is substantially lower than in public data networks, typically better than 1 in 10^5.

Local area networks can be categorised in a number of ways (Reference 1.2) but from the functional viewpoint it is convenient to consider three basic groups:

— proprietary LANs, such as micro LANs, which are relatively simple and inexpensive and which operate at data speeds of the order of hundreds of kilobits per second (Kbps). Networks of this type are designed to support the network vendor's terminal equipment;

— baseband utilities, which offer speeds in the order of Mbps, cater for a heavier traffic load and are intended to support a range of vendor-independent terminal equipment. The best known example in this category is Ethernet;

— broadband networks, which also provide a utility service but which, in addition, provide a much higher aggregate data speed, and are particularly well suited to carry mixed traffic. The Local Net System marketed by ITL Ltd is typical of this type of network.

As this grouping suggests, the technology used is also an important means of classifying LANs. With baseband LANs, data is impressed directly onto the transmission medium (coaxial cable, twisted pair wires) as a digital signal, whereas in the broadband case, the data is used to modulate an RF (radio frequency) carrier which is carried on the coaxial cable.

APPLICATION AREAS

Although LANs have developed rapidly, practical experience of planning and operating other than small network installations is still limited. Academic and other research institutions have been active in applying and developing LANs but the two most significant areas of application are office systems and factory automation.

Office Systems

Organisations such as banks and insurance companies which traditionally collect, create and transfer large quantities of information have been instrumental in making this the most advanced area in terms of LAN usage.

Stand-alone office equipment which performs a single function such as word processing is by now firmly established, but it is expected that future generations of office systems will support a wide range of fully integrated services. Figure 1.1 shows a typical range of facilities which might be expected to be available at a workstation in the near future. Integration in this context implies that the user is presented with a single interface for all services and that the services themselves involve one or more of the basic types of information (ie data, text, voice and image), for example voice-annotated text. Office systems make use of enhanced personal computers to provide powerful local computing facilities which

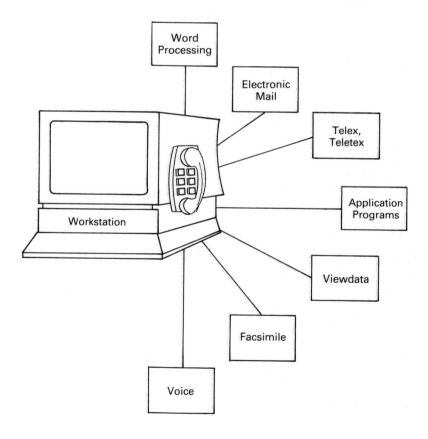

Figure 1.1

form the basis of multifunction workstations for professional, administrative and secretarial staff. Local area networks provide the necessary resource-sharing capability, document transfer facilities and services such as electronic mail. Office systems enable more ready access to information and the capability to analyse and process it more effectively than traditional methods. In consequence, management and professional staff are able to respond to changing situations more quickly and with greater confidence, while the productivity of other staff is greatly increased. Systems offering a range of non-integrated services are available but at the present time integration is at an early stage of development with a wide variation in the level of integration that is available from vendors. Integrated word processing, electronic mail and messaging are available and facilities such as integrated record- and file-processing, decision support, graphics and voice store-and-forward will progressively become available, as will voice messaging and teleconferencing.

Although the movement is toward the full integration of data, text, voice and usage information, technical difficulties and availability of suitable software are bound to make progress in some areas more rapid than in others. It is also important to consider the role that PABXs can play in office systems. Most organisations have a significant capital investment in local communications in the form of a PABX telephone network, and in recent years manufacturers of digital PABXs have begun to offer systems with a wide range of facilities and the capability to switch data as well as speech. Some commentators have seen the LAN and PABX as rivals in the office environment, but more realistically their roles are complementary. As with all systems, the relative merits of competing solutions will depend on the requirements of the situation.

Factory Automation

Factory automation is not new but it has been given greater prominence in recent years as a result of the general recessionary economy. Manufacturing plants can maintain their competitive edge only by reducing unit costs and having the flexibility to respond to changes in market demands.

Flexibility is important because the market may be limited and unable to support a large productive capacity, or the product life cycle may be short. Even in mass markets, it may only be possible for the market leaders to sustain high-volume production. This is the case in the engineering component industry for example where to enable components to be manufactured at a competitive unit cost, flexible manufacturing systems (FMSs) have been developed. These are robot-based production cells which can be rapidly rescheduled to produce attentive components from a family of parts (References 1.3 and 1.4). Robot technology enables high utilisation of the production cycle to be achieved, and the output to be matched more closely to the market demand. Spin-off advantages are that both the raw materials inventory and the finished product storage capacity needed are reduced.

The full benefit of the FMS approach is only achieved however if the movement of materials is equally efficient; one of the major difficulties in the factory environment is ensuring that the correct material is at the right place when needed. Storage and marshalling areas holding materials and products are often bottle necks because of the difficulty of retrieving specific items. Automatic storage and retrieval systems (ASRSs) are now being used to overcome this problem. These systems use computer-controlled stacker-cranes and a database which holds the description and location of all goods. Material or products can be retrieved or stored under manual control, or according to a programmed production or delivery schedule.

Further production flexibility can be achieved by integrating computer-aided design (CAD) and computer-aided engineering (CAE) with the production system to allow computer-controlled modification or substitution of products to be manufactured. See Figure 1.2.

Much of the ultimate success of factory automation will come from the integration of the various plant functions and the consequent reduction in manual intervention between processes. In particular, information management will increase.

Material resource planning (MRP) systems, for example, are becoming available and these help to plan production schedules, allocate resources, and manage raw material inventories and

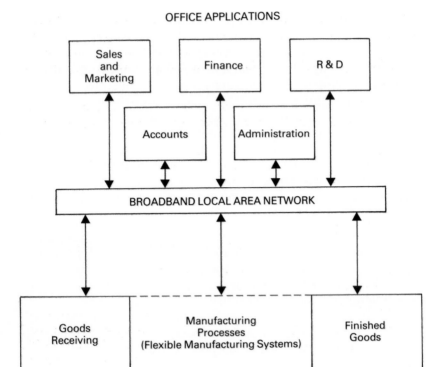

Figure 1.2

purchases. By integrating the MRP system, the production schedule can be organised and maintained by the MRP computer which can update its database on the basis of actual rather than predicted production figures.

Integration implies communication. At the present time, LANs are being used for specialist applications involving automatic testing equipment (ATE), programmable controllers and CAD/CAE systems. These are invariably proprietary, supplied by the vendor to support his equipment. But as the level of integration increases, so will the need for site-wide communication. Figure 1.3 indicates diagramatically the features of an automated factory, and shows that ultimately the so called 'front office' activities, as well as those of marketing and sales, will link into an integrated communications network.

The factory environment is inherently more complex than that of the office because of the wide range of information that must be

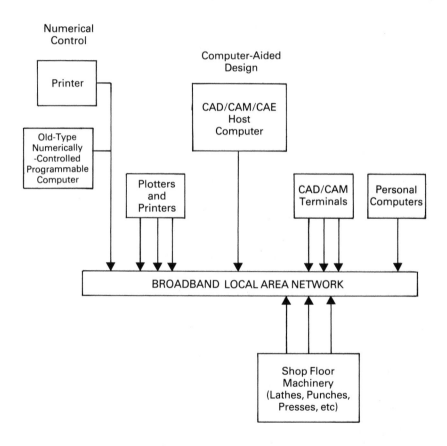

Figure 1.3   Integration of CAD/CAM/CAE with the Production System to Allow Computer-Controlled Modification or Substitution of Products to be Manufactured

handled and also its diverse transmission requirements. There are also the special problems of real-time data associated with process control applications, the wide array of interfaces and protocols, and the harshness of the environment itself. Not surprisingly, factory automation is at a less advanced stage than office systems.

2 Broadband and Baseband Networks

INTRODUCTION

Local area networks can be classified according to network topology, the means by which attached devices gain access to the network (the access protocol), and by the data transmission technology used. Since differences of approach are possible with each of these parameters, different LAN products are available, although in practice the choice for a particular application is generally surprisingly limited.

The division of LANs into broadband and baseband categories is based on transmission technology and has been the subject of lively debate in recent times. There is little substance however in some of the extreme statements that have been made in support of one technology or the other and they are now generally recognised as being complementary rather than rivals. In the product selection process, the choice between broadband and baseband technology – or indeed the way in which they might be blended – is nonetheless varied, and in this chapter the two types of LAN will be compared from a number of aspects with a view to establishing their relative merits. See Figure 2.1 for a comparison of broadband and baseband features.

MAIN FEATURES

The basic distinction between the two types of LAN is in the way the transmission medium is used. With baseband signalling, the whole cable bandwidth is used to transmit the signal and it is necessary to time-share the bandwidth between the network users.

	Bandwidth	Speed	Distance		Configuration	Bit Error Rate
Baseband	50 MHz	10 Mbps	Ring 12 miles	Bus 1 mile	Radial, Ring, Point-to-Point, Bus	1 in 10^7
Broadband	440 MHz	400 Mbps	40 miles		Tree and Bus	1 in 10^9

Figure 2.1

Using a single channel network means that to give an acceptable level of service, ie response time, a high-speed cable is required. With Ethernet for example, the cable data rate is 10 Mbps. Broadband networks on the other hand make use of frequency division multiplexing and this enables a large number of logically independent channels to be created. See Figure 2.2.

The advantage of multichannel working is that a number of different transmission modes can be integrated into a single network. Some channels may act as dedicated (point-to-point) links, others may be time-shared between a community of users using technologies similar to those employed with baseband networks, and yet others may carry speech or video. The ability of the network to carry a number of video services as well as other information is particularly important. With a baseband network it is necessary to first digitise the video signal and even with band-width compression techniques it is inevitable that the data rate required to support the service will grossly overload the network. In practice, to provide a video facility without using a broadband LAN, a separate cable television network must be used alongside the baseband LAN.

Different types of information have different characteristics, and standard protocols are unable to provide an adequate common access mechanism. With a broadband network, however, traffic having similar characteristics can be assigned to specific channels. Multichannel working can therefore be taken as an effective means of not only integrating but also segregating different types of information.

From the point of view of planned growth, the availability of multiple channels on a broadband cable also allows the system to expand gracefully because it is possible to bring additional channels into operation as needs arise without the problems of installing additional cable at each stage.

Broadband networks use coaxial cable having a bandwidth of 300-400 MHz and an aggregate data speed of the order of 300 Mbps. Depending on the data speed offered to each user therefore, the network has the potential to accommodate a large number of users. Local Net 20 for example has a capacity of 24,000 users (see

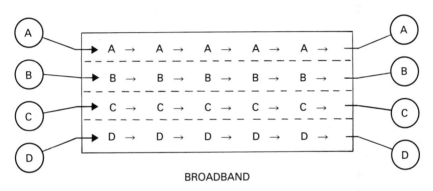

BROADBAND

Bandwidth split to carry several signals
simultaneously, eg A–D.

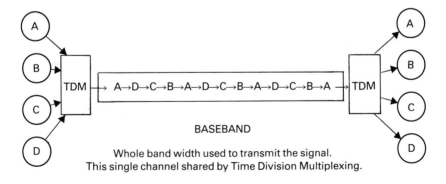

BASEBAND

Whole band width used to transmit the signal.
This single channel shared by Time Division Multiplexing.

Figure 2.2

Figure 2.3). This is provided by 120 channels, each of which can support 200 time-sharing users. The user data rate of up to 19.2 Kbps is adequate for terminal support but for more demanding applications the Local Net 40 System provides five 2 Mbps channels. In contrast, a baseband network such as Ethernet is currently limited to 1024 users, and ring networks are limited to substantially less than this figure.

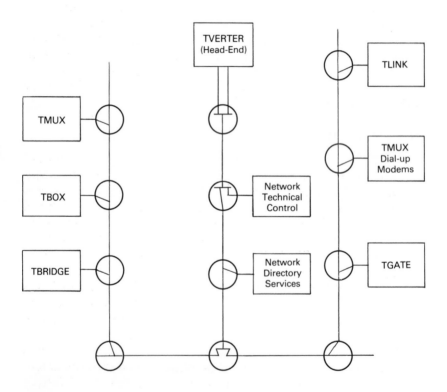

TBOX	=	Stand-alone micro-based packet communications unit
TBRIDGE	=	Connects up to four Local Net 20 channels
TGATE	=	Bridge to other external network
TLINK	=	Bridge to other local network system
TMUX	=	Enlarged TBOX providing eight user ports
TVERTER	=	Central retransmission unit

Figure 2.3   Local Net 20 – Physical Layout

For medium to large installations, the range over which a LAN will function is an important factor. Broadband networks can work over larger distances than baseband networks because amplifiers can be used to overcome signal attenuation. Ultimately, the range is set by the level of noise accumulated along the transmission route, but with good-quality amplifiers, distances in excess of 50 km are possible. In addition, the modulation techniques used in broadband transmission allow greater distances to be covered, for a comparable error performance, than baseband signalling. It is possible to use repeaters which generate the digital signals in baseband transmission, but signal dispersion – and hence increased error rate – set a substantially lower distance limitation. With Ethernet for example the maximum terminal-to-terminal distance is 2.5 km. The most significant factor in distance limitation however is the access protocol.

ACCESS PROTOCOL ISSUES

One of the most influential factors determining the performance of a LAN is the access protocol. Because of its simplicity, the most popular protocol is CSMA/CD (Carrier Sense Multiple Access with Collision Detection). This operates on a bus-type network and is sometimes referred to as the 'Ethernet' protocol. A station on the LAN which has a packet to transmit waits until the channel is 'silent' (ie free of transmissions) and then begins its own transmission. Due to the finite cable propagation time (or cable delay) it may happen that the station begins to transmit before it can detect that another station started to transmit at an earlier time, and under these conditions the protocol is designed to ensure that both stations register a collision. Both then join the channel to prevent further stations initiating a transmission before backing-off and waiting a random time before attempting a further transmission. The randomised timing is of course intended to avoid further near-simultaneous attempts. The performance of CSMA/CD depends on the normalised propagation delay, ie the ratio of the cable propagation delay to the packet transmission time (Reference 2.1). To reduce the risk of collisions, this parameter should have a low value and it is this requirement that is responsible for imposing a speed/distance restriction. The high cable data rate used in baseband systems such as Ethernet implies a short packet duration and therefore a corresponding short maximum propagation delay. This in turn restricts the maximum distance between any two stations; in the case of Ethernet this distance was given earlier as 2.5 km.

If the data rate were reduced, say, by a factor of ten, the packet duration would be increased, and for the same value of normalised propagation delay (ie protocol performance), the cable propagation – and hence the maximum cable distance – could be increased by a factor of ten. This of course is precisely what happens with a broadband LAN when the cable bandwidth is divided into logical channels. The Local Net 20 System for example uses a channel data rate of 128 Kbps and has a reputed range of 56 km. The Local Net 40 System on the other hand has a range of some 8 km. Not only do slow-speed channels give a greater range but they have the additional advantage of allowing comparatively inexpensive RF modems to be used.

The CSMA/CD protocol performs best when the network is lightly loaded. As the number of active users increases, so does the risk of collision and as more packets need to be rescheduled for transmission, the system response time naturally degrades. One of the major characteristics of the protocol is that as the load increases, there is no upper bound on the network access time and for this reason it is known as a statistical protocol. Sudden surges of traffic can also lead to excessive response times which persist after the surge has passed. This is due to the backlog of packets which must be cleared before the normal traffic flow can be supported.

In the office environment, although there may be many users, the use made of the network for information transfers represents only a small proportion of the total terminal activity and this characteristically low duty cycle or 'bursty' traffic pattern enables CSMA/CD to give satisfactory performance.

Traffic in the industrial environment on the other hand has different characteristics. In the main, the messages are much shorter – for example control signals rather than text transfers – and the traffic is more regular. Above all, this type of traffic is real-time and it is vital that the maximum packet delay has a determinable value. In the office environment, increases in response time may lead to staff complaints; in the industrial setting it can lead to disaster.

Token-passing is an access protocol which gives the necessary deterministic access time for this type of application (Reference 2.2). It is more complex than CSMA/CD but developments in integrated circuit technology have now largely overcome the cost and implementation objections. Devices attached to the network gain access by acquiring the token, which is a special packet having a data content that is prevented from occurring in any other circumstances. This enables the token to have a unique identity. When a device has the token it is free to transmit and at the end of the transmission it regenerates the token and addresses it to the next station in a predetermined sequence. Token-passing was originally conceived for ring topology networks in which the token passed sequentially from node to node around the ring. With bus structures there is of course no physical ring but the token is again passed from node to node in a cyclic fashion. This gives considerable ordering flexibility and the network is often said to have a 'logical ring' protocol. Each device in turn therefore acquires the token, and the maximum access time is bounded. Devices having no information to transmit when they receive the token simply address it to the next node. No collisions are possible with this system, so the difficulties discussed earlier and the consequential limitations do not apply to token-passing.

Whereas CSMA/CD degrades with increasing load, the performance of token-passing actually improves as the load increases because a smaller proportion of time is spent in the wasteful transfer of tokens between nodes with no information to transmit. On the other hand, since each node receives the token in turn, the average packet delay increases with the number of attached devices. In the real-time environment this can be a significant limitation of the protocol.

Digital speech and video are usually regarded as forming a separate category of information. Both present a near continuous flow of data compared with other forms of traffic and can clearly monopolise a channel. Fairly tight bounds on the maximum packet delay must be met to maintain speech intelligibility and visual clarity respectively, but due to its inherent high level of redundancy, speech can accept a higher than normal percentage of lost packets.

These characteristics are in contrast to other types of office system traffic such as text and data, and present problems in the design of protocols for integrated services (Reference 2.3).

At the present state of development, access protocols are rigid in the sense that they can be used effectively only with types of traffic which have similar transmission and delivery requirements. Although adaptive protocols are likely to emerge in the future (spurred for example by the demand for integrated office services) it is evident that multichannel broadband networks currently offer the only practical means of integrating different types of traffic in a single network. Attempts are being made to integrate speech with other office services, and Reference 2.4 gives details of a modification to the CSMA/CD back-off algorithm to accommodate speech in an Ethernet LAN.

Both the CSMA/CD and token-passing protocols are used in commercially available network products; the former in the Local Net Systems, for example, and the latter in the recently introduced LAN/1 product by Interactive Systems/3M. The CSMA/CD protocol was originally developed in the context of baseband networks, and although it is applicable to the broadband case, it is found that there is some degradation in performance in this case. In the first place, since nodes can only communicate with each other via the head-end, the propagation delay can approach twice that expected with a baseband network using the same length of cable. Secondly, the collision detection mechanism is potentially less reliable in a broadband network. Collision detection in Ethernet for example is achieved by adding a dc voltage to the data signal at the transmitting node. Any increase in dc level on the cable can then be taken as an indication that another node has started to transmit and a collision can be registered.

This scheme cannot be used with an RF system and it is usual to detect collisions by comparing the data transmitted by a device with that received from the cable on a digit-by-digit basis, a collision being indicated by any difference between the two data streams.

Although broadband design should ensure that the original level at each tap is, within limits, the same, poor design or misalignment can result in a colliding signal being too low in amplitude to be detected. On the other hand the station generating the low-level signal may receive the other signal at a high level and constantly refer to it.

Although CSMA/CD works satisfactorily on a well-engineered system, attention has been given to other protocols which seek to avoid, rather than detect, collisions (see Figure 2.4). This shows a CSMA/CD accessing scheme that employs a degree of deterministic contention resolution.

Token-passing avoids these problems although it is found that in broadband networks the average packet delay is significantly greater than in the corresponding baseband network.

NETWORK TECHNOLOGY

Coaxial cable is used for broadband LANs and for baseband utility LANs such as Ethernet. In the case of networks based on Ethernet, the cable is of a special design to ensure an adequate standard of performance in terms of access time, throughput and geographical coverage.

Due to the finite impedance that a transceiver presents to the cable when connected, reflections will occur which in certain circumstances can be misinterpreted as data or collisions. To minimise this effect (and for other reasons) 50 Ω rather than 75 Ω cable is specified. Again, particularly large reflections may occur due to transceivers being too close together and so a minimum spacing of 2.5m is specified. To assist at the installation stage, distinctive ring markings are placed at this spacing along the jacket of the cable.

As discussed earlier, collision detection is achieved by maintaining the dc level on the cable so that its dc resistance needs to be low. A 50 Ω cable is advantageous in this respect also, because for a given cable diameter, the dc resistance is lower than for a 75 Ω cable.

In contrast, broadband networks use standard 75 Ω CATV cable which is provided in large quantities and is readily available. The cost is also substantially lower than that of Ethernet cable. Equally significant is the fact that no single type of coaxial cable construction is mandatory for broadband operation so that the user has a measure of choice. Unlike Ethernet, broadband networks are designed on

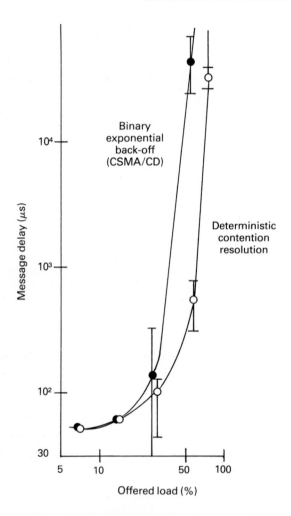

A CSMA/CD accessing scheme that employs a degree of deterministic contention resolution (DCR) can boost confidence levels to 95%. Developed by engineers at the Nippon Telegraph and Telephone Public Corporation, the technique is superior to conventional CSMA/CD, which employs a binary exponential back-off (BEB) algorithm. During normal transmission the protocol behaves like a standard CSMA/CD access method. The difference with DCR is that when collisions occur they are resolved by a form of implicit token-passing. The curves show message delay as a function of network load, for 510-bit-long messages transmitted at 10 Mbps.

Figure 2.4

an impedance-match basis so that reflections which do occur are minimal. It is therefore unnecessary to specify a minimum distance between tapping points. The degree of immunity to noise ingress is an important consideration, especially in industrial applications. Broadband networks offer significant advantages over baseband networks in this respect because of the RF modulation techniques they employ and the continuous outer conductor construction used for CATV cable. The use of other forms of coaxial cable construction will of course reduce this high level of immunity.

The means by which the CSMA/CD protocol is implemented in Ethernet-type LANs restricts the topology to that of a simple bus. The only cable components required are therefore connectors to connect sections of cable together, and the penetration or 'vampire' connectors to attach the transceivers to the cable.

Broadband networks are not restricted in this way and normally have a branching-tree topology. In addition to amplifiers and head-end frequency translators therefore, directional couplers and splitters are needed to allow the network to branch. Taps are also needed to connect the transceivers to the cable.

Cable television technology has been developed in the United States over a period of some thirty years to meet harsh environmental conditions, and at the same time promote an extremely high level of reliability. It is therefore proven technology which is readily available and offers inexpensive passive components (splitters, directional couplers and taps) from a number of manufacturers.

Baseband connector technology by contrast is comparatively new and its reliability is less certain.

DESIGN, INSTALLATION AND OPERATION

Baseband LANs are comparatively easy to implement. This is particularly so with Ethernet which is now heavily standardised and for which straightforward rules for system design and installation exist. The rules specify, for example, maximum values for the length of cable segments, the number of attachments per segment, the number of repeaters that can be used in series, and the distance between the remotest nodes.

Broadband technology is by comparison a specialist branch of

RF engineering and requires expertise at both the design and installation stages. Networks must be designed to ensure that signal
levels at the tap outputs are equalised in order that terminal equipment will function at any location in the network, and so careful
siting of amplifiers and splitters/couplers as well as selection of
correct tap values is essential.

For the potential users of broadband technology, the issue of
expertise is doubly difficult. First, since the technology is analogue
rather than digital, few organisations have technical staff with the
necessary background to undertake design; second, since broadband
engineering is comparatively new to the UK, there are few
specialist designers. As a consequence, vendors of LANs seek to
protect their position by treating design know-how as proprietary
information. The position with regard to maintenance is less difficult.
Baseband networks generally present no problems but broadband
systems require periodic testing, and some specialist training for
this purpose is necessary.

Management of the network is also more demanding in the case
of broadband networks, partly because these systems are inherently
more complex. For example, frequency management is an essential factor in the efficient operation of a broadband network.

Maintenance and management issues are considered in more
detail in a later chapter.

RELATIVE COSTS

From the point of view of the user organisation, the cost of a
network is one of its most important parameters. While it is tempting
to seek a simple answer on the comparative cost of baseband and
broadband techniques, in practice a number of factors contribute
to the overall cost, only some of which bear directly on the cost of
the network itself. More realistically, a networking proposal must
be seen in the context of its total environment before cost advantages
become clear. The cost per attachment is a commonly used criterion
nonetheless and, misleading as this may be when taken in isolation,
there is no doubt that at the present time the cost of attaching an
additional device to a broadband network is high; typically in the
order of £500. Principally this is a result of the high cost of RF
modems.

This measure does however have the merit of highlighting the main economic weakness of broadband technology, particularly when taken in the context of falling terminal prices and, more starkly, the cost of a telephone, which in an integrated environment should ideally be readily connectable to the network. Clearly a wider use of broadband technology must depend at least partly on a continuing fall in modem prices.

3 Broadband Cable and Components

INTRODUCTION

The broadband network itself consists of:

— the coaxial cable;

— the passive components which allow the network to branch;

— the amplifiers, where the size of the network requires their use;

— the head-end equipment where the system uses a single rather than a dual cable.

Cable TV components are used to implement the network and most networking product vendors supply standard 0.5 inch coaxial CATV cable. By using a solid aluminium outer conductor, an extremely high level of noise immunity is achieved but at the expense of a semi-rigid construction which can make it awkward to install in buildings where cable runs are required to be unobtrusive and blend in with the local decor.

Although standard CATV cable is very widely used, alternatives do exist and some users have successfully employed other coaxial constructions which offer greater physical flexibility and are more suited to their particular application. Selection of cable is clearly a major consideration in a network proposal, and a potential user who is likely to consider alternatives requires an understanding of the characteristics which determine the performance of the cable.

COAXIAL CABLE

The essential requirement of a transmission medium is that it should transmit signals with the minimum loss and distortion. For radio frequency signals, coaxial cable is widely used and consists of a central conductor separated from a surrounding outer conductor by a dielectric. The outer conductor is intended to prevent unwanted signals to and from the cable and is known as the screen. Figure 3.1 shows the construction of standard CATV cable.

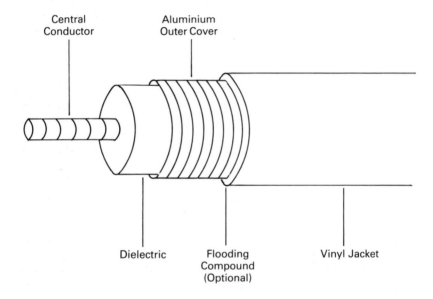

Figure 3.1   Construction of Standard CATV Cable

The characteristics of coaxial cable fall into two broad categories; electrical, and mechanical and physical.

Electrical Characteristics

Characteristic Impedance

This is the impedance presented by a correctly terminated section of the cable and for broadband applications (and of course, CATV use) has a value of 75 Ω. The value is determined by the ratio of the diameter over the dielectric to that over the inner conductor, as well as by the dielectric material. Due to normal manufacturing tolerances, the impedance will vary over the length of the cable but normally by no more than ± 2 Ω.

Attenuation

Signal attenuation, or loss, is due to losses in the two conductors and the dielectric. Conductor loss is proportional to the square root of the frequency whereas dielectric loss is proportional to frequency. Figure 3.2 shows the attenuation/frequency relationship for a

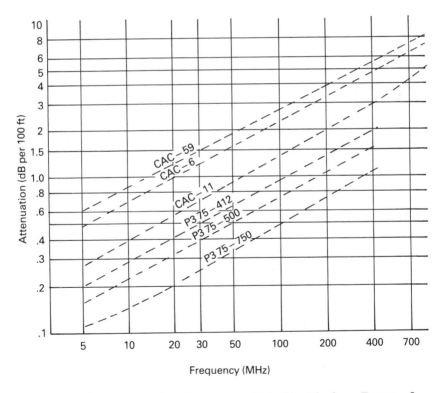

Figure 3.2   Attenuation/Frequency Relationship for a Range of Cable Sizes

range of cable sizes. Notice that the cable size is determined by the diameter over the screen.

To minimise loss, the conductor material should have a low resistivity, and solid copper makes an ideal choice since it is also flexible and easy to process. Aluminium is cheaper but has a higher resistivity than copper and reduced tensile strength. It is also susceptible to environmental deterioration, but the dielectric should provide adequate protection from damage.

Copper-clad aluminium is an acceptable alternative to solid copper and, because the skin effect increasingly confines the current flow to the surface of the conductor as the frequency increases, its electrical properties are similar. Both solid copper and copper-clad aluminium are used in CATV cable.

Yet another alternative is copper-clad steel. Again the electrical properties are similar to those of solid copper and it is often used for drop cables because the centre conductor of the cable can act as the centre pin of F-type connectors.

Return Loss

Random variations in the characteristic impedance along the length of the cable will set up local reflections and the net effect can be measured at the input to the cable. The return loss is the ratio of the input voltage to the resultant reflected voltage and for a good quality cable it should have a value of between 30dB and 40dB.

As well as reflections arising from random variations in the physical dimensions of the cable and the homogeneity of the dielectric, periodic irregularities can also occur along a cable length. These are due to slight eccentricities in the rotating components of the cable-manufacturing machinery and can lead to excessive signal attenuation (known as 'suckouts') at localised frequencies. For this reason, all lengths should be frequency-swept before installation.

Velocity of Propagation

This is the velocity at which a single frequency is transmitted along the cable. The discussion in Chapter 2 showed that propagation delay is an important parameter when a CSMA/CD protocol is used, and a high value of propagation velocity is therefore desirable. Typically, CATV cable has a value between 0.8 and 0.9 that of light in vacuum.

Screening Efficiency

One of the most important considerations in cable selection is the degree of protection the construction offers against electrical interference from external sources and, equally important, leakage from the system which may interfere with other nearby electrical equipment. Noise ingress is a potential problem in industrial environments where heavy electrical machinery may be in use, but signal egress from the network can be as great a problem in, for example, airport installations where interference may adversely affect navigation and radio services. Even in apparently benign office situations, good protection is needed to reduce system down-time due to noisy office equipment.

In principle, the coaxial type of construction is effective in preventing noise ingress and egress since the screen can be connected to earth potential, and interfering currents will be confined to the screen earth-return circuit. In practice the screen is not an ideal conductor and shielding is less than complete. The objective of cable design then is to cause most of the interfering current due to external sources to flow in the screen and as little as possible to be induced in the centre conductor of the cable.

The effectiveness of the screen is generally measured by the surface transfer impedance (Z_T) – or simply the transfer impedance – and is defined as the open-circuit voltage included in the centre conductor of a unit length of the cable by a one ampere screen current. This topic is discussed further in a later section.

Mechanical and Physical Characteristics

Mechanical and physical characteristics include cable pull strength, crush strength and cable weight, in addition to the characteristics mentioned below.

Abrasion Resistance

The cable needs to be protected from damage during installation and this is one function of the sheath. Polyethylene has good water-resisting properties and for this reason is used extensively as the sheathing material for cables to be installed externally. Its abrasion resistance is not entirely satisfactory however and at least one manufacturer has developed a bonded sheath. This consists of an inner polyethylene skin with an outer polypropylene layer. The outer skin is highly abrasion resistant and its low frictional resistance makes the pulling of cable through ducts easier.

Environmental Resistance

The cable sheath must provide adequate protection against damage from the environment throughout the life of the cable. The level and type of protection needed will naturally depend on the particular environment concerned, but for external installations the problem of water ingress should be considered (cable ducts will often be subject to flooding), and for internal installation the degree of fire retardance of the cable and gases which are either acidic or toxic should be taken into account. Other environmental damage that needs to be considered is rodent attack, extremes of temperature, and damaging atmospheres. In most cases, manufacturers are able to provide cable constructions which give an adequate level of protection.

Flexibility

Flexibility is an important consideration in the installation of the cable. Standard CATV technology utilises semi-rigid cable. This can be advantageous for some purposes, for example the cable can be installed without the need for cable-trays and can be simply clipped to walls. But there are also disadvantages; the cable is more difficult to handle than a fully flexible cable and, in particular, the comparatively large minimum bending radius needed to avoid damaging the cable (typically $10 \times$ the cable diameter) can make it difficult to negotiate architectual features in buildings.

In the UK, the emphasis on ducted cabling for cable television rather than aerial cable as in the United States has led to the development of a more flexible semi-airspaced dielectric cable which is likely to find increasing application in broadband LAN installations.

Cable Construction

Cables differ in their construction by the way in which the dielectric is formed and the screening is provided.

Dielectrics

In order to minimise the dielectric loss component, the material selected needs to have a low permittivity. It must also have mechanical strength and be flexible. Electrically, air is the best dielectric and it is used with an appropriate material, usually polyethylene, to give a composite material with acceptable electrical and mechanical properties.

In the past, solid polyethylene dielectrics have been used for TV distribution cables, but the losses have generally been regarded as excessive and foamed polyethylene is more widely used. Maximum use is made of air as the dielectric material in the semi-airspaced cable construction shown in Figure 3.3(a), which employs a five-cell cartwheel arrangement. The centre conductor is covered and supported along its length with solid polyethylene, and this allows the cable to be flexed without distorting the cable and hence altering its characteristic impedance. The main disadvantage of this construction is that water can easily travel along the cells if the cable is damaged.

An alternative semi-airspaced construction uses polyethylene discs mounted periodically along the length of the cable as shown in Figure 3.3(b). The centre conductor is again covered with polyethylene but the construction makes the bending characteristics inferior to those of the five-cell cables.

Screens

The outer conductor determines the screening efficiency of the cable which may be subject to the following forms of interference:

— electrostatic induction (due principally to high voltages present in industrial environments);

— magnetic induction (due to high currents present in electrical machinery in industrial environments);

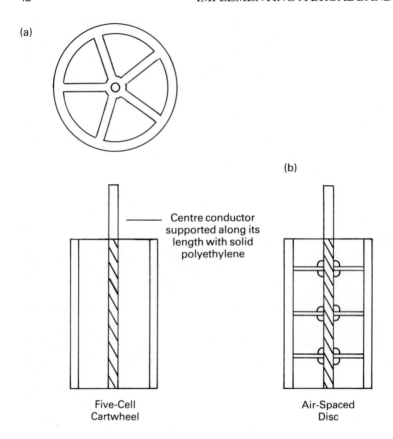

Figure 3.3

—   electromagnetic induction (a high-frequency effect caused
     by the cable acting as an antenna).

Notice that electromagnetic induction is the only mechanism
which leads to signal egress and is due to the cable system acting as
a radiating antenna. In practice this is also the most important form
of interference, and one of the most effective means of providing
screening is to use a seamless tube containing no openings as the
outer conductor of the cable.

If the screening material were a perfect conductor, the screening would also be perfect, but in practice a current flows on the inner surface of the screen. This phenomenon is known as the 'skin effect' and affects the high frequency resistance of the inner and outer conductors, and also the screening and attenuation properties of the outer conductor. As the frequency increases, the current on the cable is increasingly confined to the outer surface of the inner conductor (see Figure 3.4(a)) and the inner surface of the outer conductor (see Figure 3.4(b)). The 'skin effect' is normally expressed in the form of skin depth and this can be calculated using the mathematical formula given in Figure 3.4(c).

Aluminium is used in CATV cable for reasons of cost and weight, but a disadvantage of the material is its poor corrosion properties. Manufacturers normally use a viscous 'flooding compound' between the screen and the sheath (see Figure 3.1) and this is able to seal any minor damage sustained by the sheath which would otherwise allow corrosion to develop.

For many applications, cable flexibility is essential and for this purpose a metal braid may be used as the screen. This type of construction is cheap and widely used and is shown in Figure 3.5. The coverage provided by the braid is not complete and the resulting apertures provide the means for the centre conductor to be capacitively coupled to an external circuit. Two inductive components are introduced by the braid; one due to the holes and the other due to the woven nature of the braid. These act in opposition to one another and by increasing the optical coverage – which might be thought to *reduce* the transfer impedance (Z_T) – the effect can be to *increase* Z_T.

It is possible to optimise the braid so that the two inductive components are approximately equal in magnitude, and this leads to an improved shielding performance as shown in Figure 3.6, but at the expense of greater electric field coupling through the screen. The screening efficiency can also be improved by using more than one braid. Braids are normally made of aluminium or copper.

An alternative approach is to use metal tape – again aluminium or copper – as the screen. This is applied longitudinally and either overlapped at the edges or welded. Welding presents a number of

(a) Skin depth on inner conductor

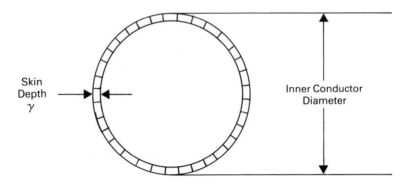

(b) Skin depth on outer conductor

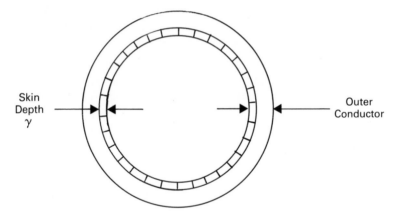

(c) Skin depth formula

$$\text{Skin depth } \gamma = \sqrt{\frac{2 \, P_C}{\omega \mu_O \, \mu_{rc}}}$$

where P_C =   resistivity of conductor
        ω = 2π f, where f is frequency in Hz
        μ_O =   absolute permeability = $4 \pi \times 10^{-7}$ H/m
        μ_{rc} =   relative permeability of the conductor

Figure 3.4   Skin Effect

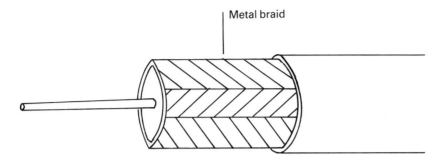

Figure 3.5   Metal Braid Screen

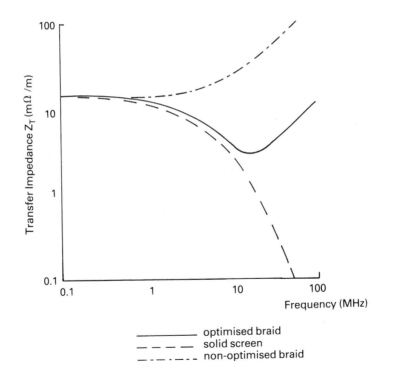

Figure 3.6   Improved Shielding Performance of Optimised Braid

problems since the quality of the weld has a marked effect on the screening efficiency. At the same time, the degree of overlap and the quality of the contact between the edges in the alternative construction are equally critical. In both cases, repeated flexing of the cable can lead to breaks in the tape or failure of the weld.

The most widely used construction where a high level of screening is required is tape overlaid with one or more braids. The tape is generally thinner (approximately 0.05mm compared with 0.15mm) and the overlapped edges are held in good contact by the braid.

The screening efficiency may be improved, as before, by using multiple tape and braid combinations. The screening methods which have been discussed are also effective against electrostatic and magnetic induction. The former is dependent on penetration of the screen by the electric field and, provided a good conductor is used, interference should be minimal. Capacitive coupling due to holes in the screen with braids may present problems, but in practice adequate protection is provided by ensuring a high optical coverage with multiple braids, or by using a metal tape.

Magnetic induction can be minimised by using a tape material having a high permeability, such as mu metal, so that the interfering field is effectively confined to the screen. Protection against magnetic induction is also provided by the currents which are set up in the screen by the magnetic field itself since these produce their own magnetic field which opposes the primary field. At the same time, eddy currents will be set up in the screen at high frequencies and these also tend to counteract the interfering field.

Screening is a complex subject and it is only possible to treat it in outline in this work. Readers wishing to study this topic in greater detail are referred to the authoritative account given by Vance (Reference 3.1). Reference 3.2 also deals with optimised and super-screened cables.

DROP CABLES

The broadband network itself will make use of either the standard 0.5 inch CATV cable or one of the alternative coaxial cable constructions such as the five-cell cartwheel. In order to drop from a tap to a network interface unit however, it is normal to use a coaxial cable such as RG-6. This offers greater physical flexibility than the CATV cable – which is clearly essential – but at the expense of reduced electrical performance. For example, the attenuation of RG-6 cable is typically 11dB/100m, and the noise immunity is in excess of eight times less than that of standard 0.5 inch CATV cable.

Normally the length of drop cable involved does not exceed 20m and this reduction in performance is not significant, but in electrically noisy environments (or in special cases where noise egress is important) it may be necessary to use highly-screened drop cable to maintain the inherent superior performance of a broadband network.

The RG-6 cable uses a copper-coated steel inner conductor, a foamed polyethylene dielectric, and aluminium braiding and tape as the screen.

CABLE CONNECTORS

Connectors are potentially the weakest link in the network since a poor connection can lead to troublesome RF faults which can be difficult to locate and rectify. It is important therefore that only the highest quality connectors are used. The cost differential between these and poor quality connectors is small, and is in any event amply justified on the grounds of increased reliability.

Two systems of connector are in use; one for connecting the 0.5 inch cable to the broadband network components (ie taps, splitters and amplifiers), and the other for providing connections from the tap output side of the network.

The first system of connectors are robust and provide a secure watertight connection. One type of connector uses a screen mechanism which seizes the outer conductor of the cable and allows the centre conductor to extend through the body of the connector. The connector is then screened into the housing of the tap or amplifier and the centre conductor is secured on a screen terminal block set into the body of the component housing. An improved version of this type of connector seizes the outer conductor of the cable in a similar way, and another screen mechanism seizes the centre conductor. This mechanism has a solid brass pin (or 'stinger') attached to it. The pin extends through the connector body and this, rather than the centre conductor, is secured on the terminal block. Figures 3.7(a) and (b) show these two types of connector.

For connection from the tap outputs, the much simpler and less robust 'F' connectors are used. Again, the connector seizes only the out braid and jacket of the coaxial cable (but this time by a crimping action) and the centre conductor of the cable extends through the body to become the centre contact. The centre conductor of the RG-6 drop cable is made of steel and its mechanical properties make it resistant to physical deformation. This makes it suitable for a push fit into the matching half of the connector. Figure 3.7(c) shows a male 'F' connector.

SPLITTERS, DIRECTIONAL COUPLERS AND TAPS

Splitters and directional couplers are passive devices which enable the network to branch. The basic splitter (see Figure 3.7(d)) divides the input power equally between its two output ports. This gives a 3dB loss over each transmission path although in practice this will be increased to approximately 3.5dB due to internal losses. Splitters can also be used in combinations to produce three- and four-way outputs and these are available as standard units from manufacturers. The loss of any input will depend however on how many times the signal is divided and, as Figure 3.8(a) shows, regional losses occur in the three-way splitter.

Splitters are bi-directional devices and they can be used to combine signals rather than split them. The head-end combiner is the most frequent application of the bi-directional characteristic of the splitter, and this is discussed in Chapter 4.

Directional couplers are used where part of the input power is to be directed (or tapped off) either to a drop cable or a feeder cable. Directional couplers have only a main and a tap output and are available with a range of coupling values, the correct value of which must be selected to give the required signal level at the tap output. The device is specified by a number of parameters:

— insertion loss (dB);
— tap value (dB);
— isolation loss (dB);

(a)   Feed Through ('VSF')

A device that seizes only the outer conductor of the coaxial cable. The cable centre conductor extends through this type of connector and is retained within the equipment housing.

(b)   Pin Type ('Stinger')

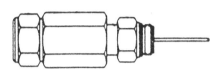

A connector that seizes both the outer and centre conductor. This device has an additional feature not found in the feed through type consisting of a solid brass pin which seizes and retains the cable centre conductor. The pin then extends through the body and is retained within the equipment housing.

(c)   Male 'F'

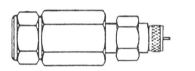

This device is used when it is necessary to have a male 'F' connection at the end of the cable. This connector has the same features as the pin type, splice and female 'F' in that both centre and outer conductors of the cable are seized.

(d)

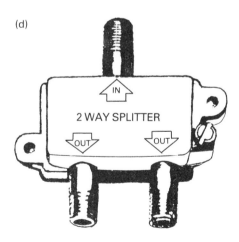

Figure 3.7

— return loss (dB).

In addition, the operating bandwidth should be given; it is normally 5-400 MHz.

Referring to Figure 3.8(b); insertion loss (A-B) is the signal attenuation across the device in the main direction of signal flow, and the tap value is the signal loss from the input port of the tap output. The isolation loss (B-C) is the attenuation between the output port and the tap port, and is typically greater than 30dB. It is this high loss between the output and tap ports which gives the device its directional character, ie a signal applied to the output port would produce little output at the tap port. The return loss, as in the case of cable, is a measure of the matching properties of the device and should have a value of at least 30dB. It should also be noticed that, as the coupler essentially partitions the input power between two output ports, the insertion loss is not constant but depends on the value of the tap loss, increasing in value as the tap value decreases.

It is usual to power amplifiers in cable TV systems from the cable itself rather than locally, since in many instances this will not be possible. Provision is therefore made for splitters and couplers to pass mains frequency power along with the RF signal where they are designed for outdoor installation. Live-powering of amplifiers is also convenient for LANs, and splitter and directional coupler specifications should include their mains frequency current-carrying capacity and the mains frequency hum modulation.

Taps are similar to directional couplers except that more than one tap output is provided, and they are used to tap off a proportion of the input power to feed terminal equipment via drop cables. A range of tap values is available for each tap within a product range and two, four and eight tap output versions are normally supplied. The tapping value range is normally wide, for example 11-35dB in 3dB steps.

For the same reason as with a directional coupler, the insertion loss of a tap depends on the tap value but additionally it depends on the number of tap outputs. Figure 3.9 shows the principal tap parameters.

(a) Regional losses occuring in a three-way splitter

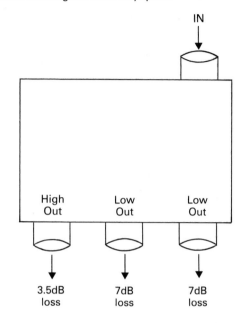

(b)

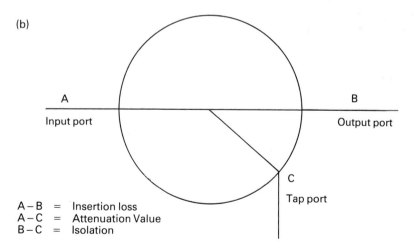

A – B = Insertion loss
A – C = Attenuation Value
B – C = Isolation

Figure 3.8

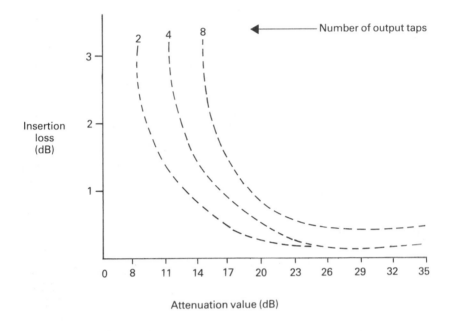

Figure 3.9   Principal Tap Parameters

MINIATURE TAPS AND SPLITTERS

Traditionally, broadband components have been developed for external use and to withstand extremes of climatic conditions. They therefore tend to be of a robust but bulky construction. For interior applications, where environmental conditions are more controlled, a less robust range of splitters and taps is generally available and these are usually known as 'miniature' components.

AMPLIFIERS

Several types of amplifier are used in cable TV systems, but the high-quality mid-split trunk amplifier is the type most frequently used in broadband LANs.

This is a modulator unit and is generally supplied in a cast aluminium weather-proof housing which makes the amplifier suitable for external installation. As well as having provisions for forward and reverse amplifier modules, the unit can accommodate pads (ie fixed-value attenuators), equalisers, and filters to separate up-stream and down-stream traffic signals. Test points are also provided together with a power supply which can be powered from the cable itself. Figure 3.10(a) shows a basic trunk amplifier and Figure 3.10(b) a variant known as a bridge amplifier. This modification enables the main signal to be split and separately amplified and is useful where a multi-trunk network is to be implemented.

Normal trunk amplifier gains are between 22 and 28dB with a normal control which allows the gain to be varied by between 8 and 10dB. Cable TV network design has become standardised with time and this limited gain range together with the use of pads proves adequate in practice.

Where a system uses a number of amplifiers in cascade, consideration must be given to the noise and distortion characteristics of the individual amplifier. Trunk amplifiers typically have a noise figure of between 7 and 10dB. The noise figure is the amount of noise generated in the amplifier over and above the input noise. The signal-to-noise ratio (SNR) is a more important measure of the quality of performance than the noise level alone but, since data signals are complex, it is more usual to compare the noise level with that of the unmodulated carrier. This is known as the carrier-to-noise ratio (CNR).

Distortion arises because the relationship between the output and input signal levels is not perfectly linear. Second-order, or harmonic, distortion is not generally significant because the push/pull design of the amplifier minimises the effect. Third-order distortion on the other hand can become a limiting factor. It includes triple-beat distortion (the sum and difference of any three carrier frequencies), and cross-modulation (the modulation produced on one carrier by a number of other carriers) and, like second-order distortion, is dependent on the amplifier signal level.

Trunk amplifiers are of course intended primarily for television applications and published specifications are applicable to video rather than data signals. Where it is necessary to calculate the distortion performance of an amplifier carrying data signals therefore, it is common practice to assume that the maximum number of

(a)   Trunk Amplifier

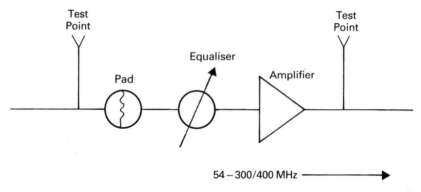

(b)   Bridge Amplifier

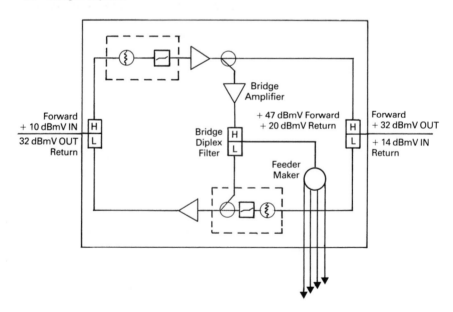

Figure 3.10

television carriers in the cable bandwidth under consideration are active (remember, cross-modulation depends on the number of active channels). The number of active carriers in a broadband LAN varies statistically and this makes such a calculation hardly accurate, but in practice it is found that the actual performance is better than predicted.

Although noise and distortion are important – they in fact limit the geographical size of a network – even comparatively large area networks seldom use sufficient cascaded amplifiers to present problems. For example, the campus-wide network for Brown University (see Reference 3.3) used only six cascaded amplifiers. The CNR and distortion should always be measured in an amplified LAN however to ensure that these parameters are within specification (see Chapter 4).

Appendix 2 gives expressions for the overall CNR and cross-modulation of both cascaded identical and dissimilar amplifiers, and Reference 3.4 treats noise and distortion in a more detailed manner.

4 System Design Principles

INTRODUCTION

The design of a broadband cable network is considerably more complex that that of a baseband network. This is partly because the level of expertise required is higher but also because of the lack of common standards in this area. One effect of this, already mentioned, is that vendors and independent cable designers tend to treat their own techniques and standards as proprietary information.

An important and early decision for the user organisation is therefore whether the vendor, or an external consultant, is to be responsible for the design and installation of the network, or whether the scale of communications operations within the organisation warrants the development of in-house expertise.

In this chapter, a brief review of some design considerations and commissioning tests for local area networks will be given. The intention is to give the prospective customer of a broadband system some idea of the complexities involved in broadband network design and its heavy reliance on RF engineering skills to achieve this. (In practice most customers would call on the expert advice of specialists within this field; see the section on design and installation in Chapter 5.)

NETWORK STRUCTURES

Broadband networks have a branching tree topology as shown in Figure 4.1. Here the centre cable acts as a trunk with distribution cables emanating from appropriate points via directional couplers.

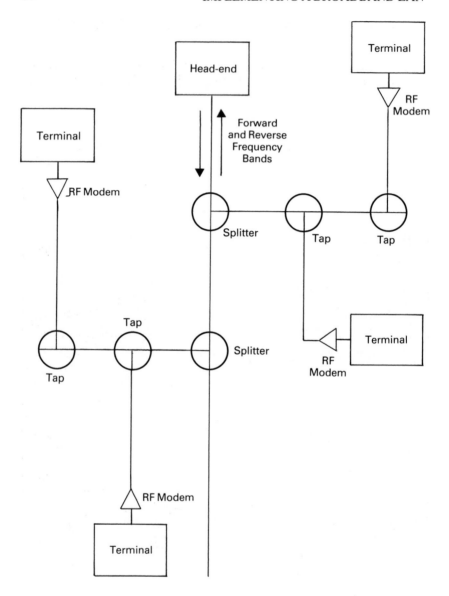

**Figure 4.1   Taps and Splitters used to Establish Branches in A Tree
Topology**

This arrangement is typical of a network serving a single building as shown in Figure 4.2.

Frequently the site will require more than one trunk cable; for example where a number of buildings exist in a factory complex or

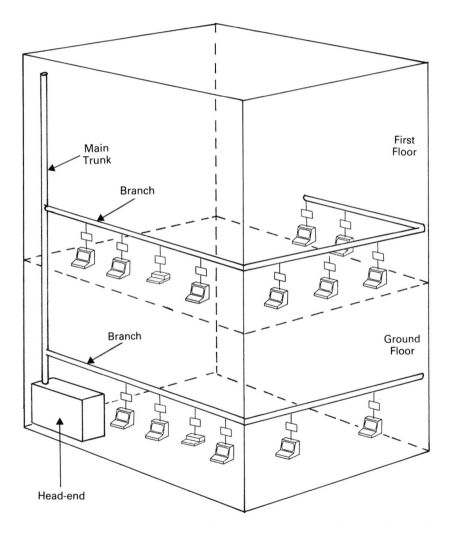

Figure 4.2   Typical Broadband Network Serving a Single Building

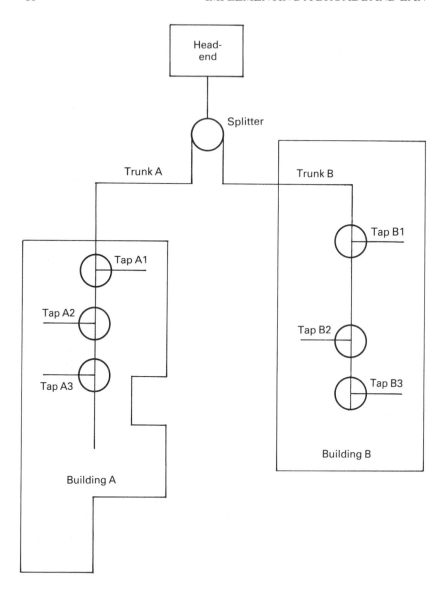

Figure 4.3   Using a Splitter at the Head-end to Create Two Trunks A and B (in the Event of Trunk A being Damaged, B will Remain Operational)

a campus. In this case, a splitter can be located at the head-end as shown in Figure 4.3. In fact this arrangement is desirable in itself because it improves the reliability of the system. In the example shown, damage to trunk A will only affect users in building A. In addition, the use of multiple trunk cables will reduce the number of amplifiers needed in the system. Trunks can be created with splitters or directional couplers; splitters should be used where equally loaded trunks are to be used, otherwise a greater reach for one trunk can be achieved using a coupler.

Splitters can also be used to increase reliability in distribution sections of the network. Instead of using a single cable to distribute taps on each floor in the illustration given in Figure 4.2, for example, a four-way splitter can be used to give four independent legs. This has two advantages; it enables each leg to be phased-in as required, and cable damage sustained on leg A, for example, will only affect taps on that leg.

HEAD-END STRUCTURES

The system head-end can take several forms. At the simplest level, it can be the passive loop-round used in dual cable networks, or a frequency translator in the case of a single cable system. In medium to large scale installations, however, the head-end will need to provide a range of facilities, and for a single cable system will typically take the form shown in Figure 4.4. Several comments may be made about this structure:

(a) The return amplifier is used to amplify and equalise the return signal, and adds flexibility to the system especially where un-amplified trunks are used. Frequently the forward amplifier module is omitted because the translator itself has sufficient gain to provide the required head-end output signal level.

(b) Test facilities are needed so that signals can be injected into the network and the reverse signal can be monitored. Notice that directional couplers are used for this purpose and should be mounted either in the forward or reverse direction as required.

(c) Off-air video signals may be distributed by the network as shown. The signal does not in this case need to be translated,

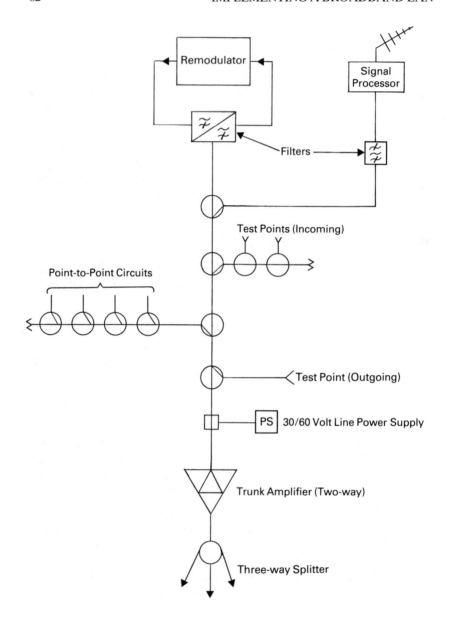

Figure 4.4   Single Cable System/Head-end Features

but signal processing will be required to frequency convert the signal to the appropriate cable channel.

(d)   Some networks will include point-to-point services and these too do not require the use of a translator. The 'head-end' for the circuits may in fact be remotely located from the main head-end via an extension cable.

(e)   Where amplifiers other than that at the head-end are used in the system, it is generally desirable to follow cable television practice and power these from the cable rather than locally. This enables a secure power supply to be situated at the head-end, together with a standby power supply if needed.

REVIEW OF SYSTEM DESIGN PRINCIPLES

Designers of cable networks have several objectives. These principally are to ensure that the following parameters are within specified design limits:

—   the signal level at each tap output in the downstream direction is the same;

—   the signal level in the upstream direction at the head-end is independent of the tap position;

—   the signal level at the tap outputs and the head-end are independent of the cable channel in use.

In this way, full mobility of terminal equipment, without the need to alter transmit and receive signal levels, is obtained. In addition, the designer should incorporate sufficient signal headroom to allow for any future expansion of the network.

In order to illustrate some aspects of the design process, the layout of Figure 4.5(a) will be used. This shows part of a four-trunk network. The head-end output signal level is assumed to be 32dBmV and the required signal level at each tap output is to be between –2dBmV and –6dBmV. For simplicity, standard 0.5 inch CATV cable will be assumed to be used throughout with an attenuation of 4.3dB/100m at 300 MHz.

The design of broadband networks owes much to the techniques developed to design cable television systems (Reference 4.1). The principal differences result from the much smaller geographical coverage of the network, and hence fewer amplifiers needed, and of course the greater emphasis on the return signal and the variety of traffic concerned.

Moving from the head-end in Figure 4.5(a), the signal level at the input to the directional coupler is readily calculated to be 24.1dBmV. Assuming no expansion along leg A is envisaged, the coupler value has been selected to be 7dB. The tap output signal level is therefore 17.1dBmV, reducing to 13.7dBmV at the input to the first tap. A 17dB tap at this point will then give a tap output of –3.3dBmV. The value of the second tap on this leg (also 17dB) can be determined in the same way.

Looking now at distribution leg B, and using the insertion loss values given in the diagram, the attenuation between the head-end and the furthest tap can be calculated to be 30.1dB. If a 7dB tap were used in this position, the tap output signal level would be –5.1dBmV. Although this is acceptable, the solution is marginal because no further expansion on this leg would be possible because of the low signal level.

The signal level at the input to the two-way splitter is 10.3dBmV however, and as this is the nominal input level for an amplifier, one might conveniently be sited at this point. With a gain of 22dB this gives sufficient signal headroom to accommodate a reasonable degree of expansion along leg B. If further expansion along the trunk (ie between the head-end and the amplifier) is envisaged, the amplifier can be moved, say, 3dB (ie approximately 70m) nearer the head-end, and the input signal temporarily padded down to 10dBmV. Remember that any expansion will require couplers or splitters to be used and these will introduce insertion loss.

The tap values for leg B are selected in the same way as those for leg A. Figure 4.5(b) shows the amplifier network together with the tap values and output signal levels.

Another factor which must be considered in the design of the forward (or downstream) path is the effect of cable tilt, ie the increase of cable attenuation with frequency. In Figure 4.5(b), the tap values have been selected so that the output signal levels are within the specified limits at 300 MHz. Assuming the lowest forward

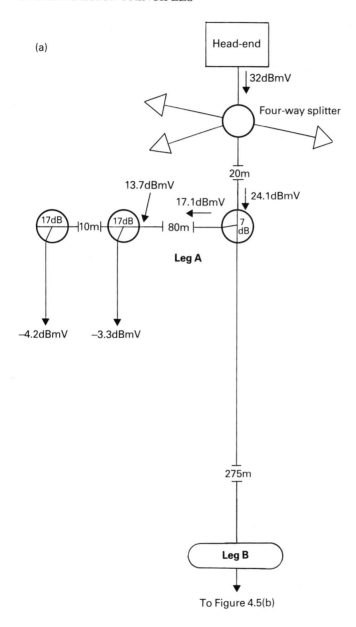

Figure 4.5 (continues)

(b)

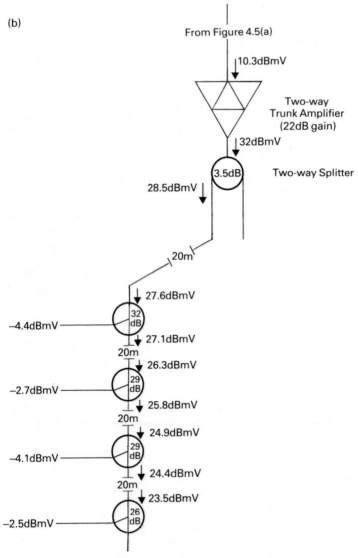

From Figure 4.5(a)

↓10.3dBmV

Two-way
Trunk Amplifier
(22dB gain)

↓32dBmV

3.5dB   Two-way Splitter

28.5dBmV ↓

20m

↓ 27.6dBmV

−4.4dBmV ——— 32 dB

↓ 27.1dBmV

20m

↓ 26.3dBmV

−2.7dBmV ——— 29 dB

↓ 25.8dBmV

20m

↓ 24.9dBmV

−4.1dBmV ——— 29 dB

↓ 24.4dBmV

20m

↓ 23.5dBmV

−2.5dBmV ——— 26 dB

Assume 0.5 inch standard CATV cable at 4.3dB/100m at 300 Mhz
Assume tap loss = 0.5dB

Figure 4.5

path frequency to be used is 160 MHz, and that at this frequency the attenuation is 3.1dB/100m, the signal level at the output of the furthest tap in Figure 4.5(b) will rise by 4.5dB (notice that the passive components in the network have an insertion loss which is effectively independent of frequency and this 'flat' loss can be ignored in the calculation).

In this illustrative example, the cable tilt has caused the signal levels at the tap outputs to exceed the specification. The problem can be overcome however by using equalisers, alone or in conjunction with the manual tilt control provided in the amplifier.

An equaliser is a passive device which introduces attenuation that is frequency dependent. In this way, by selecting the correct equaliser, the overall tilt can be reduced to zero. The amplifier tilt control allows the output signal levels to be varied with frequency. Normally, trunk amplifiers can compensate for a tilt of up to 5dB.

Equaliser modules can be accommodated in both the forward and reverse directions of trunk amplifiers, but where a section of the network is not amplified, equalisers which can be fitted into the cable run as required are available.

It is important to emphasise that a flat frequency spectrum will only be obtained at specific points in the network. In Figure 4.5(b) for example, an equaliser can be used at the amplifier to give a flat input spectrum, but the tilt will remain on the cable preceding the amplifier. Similarly if the output of the amplifier is pre-tilted so that the frequency spectrum is flat at the last tap in leg B, other points along the leg will exhibit tilt.

So far, only the forward transmission path has been considered. The reverse path must also be examined because the cable attenuation in this direction will be less than in the forward direction. In an example, the tap input signal level is assumed to be 42dBmV and the required signal at the head-end test point, at least 10dBmV. Figure 4.6 shows the return signal levels at various points in the network assuming that at the highest reverse frequency the cable attenuation is 2.5dB/100m. For the unamplified section of the network (leg A) the head-end amplifier must provide a gain of 25dB and this must be taken into account in determining the gain of the trunk amplifier to achieve the necessary head-end signal level

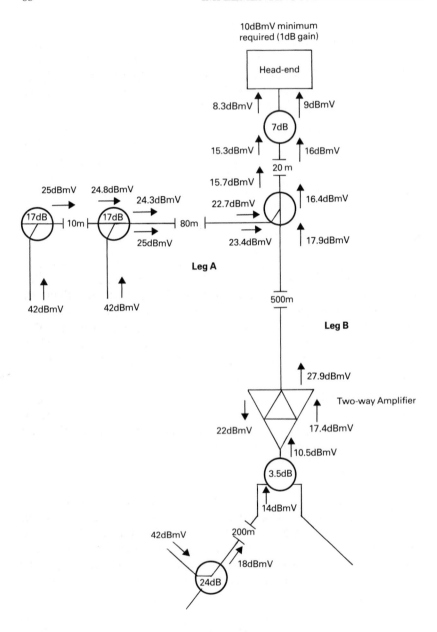

Figure 4.6

for taps on leg B. Alternatively, the head-end amplifier may be omitted and the forward path head-end signal increased at the translator. Whether this is possible will depend of course on the head-end gain which will be needed for the unamplified leg of the network. As in the case of forward path, the reverse path will also need to be considered for equalisation.

This simple example shows that in any single-cable network, the forward and reverse path performances are interdependent. The differences in the attenuation of the two paths frequently necessitate repeated calculations for the two directions (ie selection of different tap values) and with a large network this may represent a significant allowance for design time.

SYSTEM DESIGN LEVELS

Where a large number of amplifiers is to be used in a network, distortion must be considered. Unfortunately, specifications for amplifiers relate only to television applications (since they are intended mainly for the CATV industry) and this information cannot readily be related to situations in which data is being transmitted. At the same time, to achieve an acceptable picture quality, it is necessary to operate at higher signal levels when transmitting video information rather than data.

A broadband network which is intended to be used for video applications is therefore normally designed using signal levels appropriate to cable television transmission on the assumption that the network will then perform satisfactorily with data.

SYSTEM ALIGNMENT

Following installation, the system must be correctly aligned. This involves adjustment of the equalisation and of the gain controls both at the head-end and at amplifiers throughout the system. Alignment is necessary because component tolerances and, more particularly, uncertainty as to the exact length of cable sections prevent precise calculations at the design stage. To carry out the alignment, the following test equipment is needed:

— a sweep generator. This provides a semi-wave signal whose frequency increases linearly with time within a set bandwidth and on a repetitive basis. For broadband work, the generator should cover the frequency range 5 MHz to 450 MHz. The amplitude of the signal and the sweep rate should be capable of being varied, and a manually varied fixed frequency output signal should be available;

— a spectrum analyser. This displays the frequency spectrum of a signal on a CRT and enables frequency components in the signal to be measured both in terms of amplitude and frequency.

Forward Path Alignment

The equalisation of the network can be carried out so that the signal spectrum is flat at the output of an amplifier, at the input of an amplifier, or at the mid-point of the cable section between adjacent amplifiers. The first option has practical attractions because the equaliser and the point at which the signal is monitored are at the same location and equalisation can be carried out by one person. Mid-span equalisation is to be preferred however, because this reduces the variation in signal level due to tilt along the length of cable concerned. The disadvantage of this approach is that two people are needed to make the adjustments.

The procedure is as follows: the sweep generator is connected to the head-end test point, with the signal level at the design value and the sweep range adjusted to cover the cable bandwidth. Using an appropriate equaliser, the tilt control is then adjusted until the signal spectrum at the tap situated half-way to the next amplifier in the section is as flat as possible. After equalisation, the gain of the amplifier is adjusted so that the output signal level is within the design limits, normally ± 1dB.

The spectrum analyser is then moved to the next mid-span tap and the procedure repeated.

Reverse Path Alignment

This is similar to the forward path procedure. In this case, the sweep generator is connected to the tap furthest from the head-end and, using the design input signal level, each return amplifier in turn is adjusted so that the mid-span tap signal spectrum is flat (usually within 12dB) and the signal level is within specification.

Unamplified Path

These sections of the network should be aligned first because the return head-end amplifier and the translator gain are the only points of flexibility, and both affect the amplified paths.

OTHER SYSTEM TESTS

Alignment of the system is essential if the network is to give reliable service. In addition, tests should be performed to ensure that the performance is within the design specification.

Measurement of CNR

The limitations imposed by noise and distortion in amplified systems have already been discussed in Chapter 3, and the first two tests are intended to quantify their effects.

The carrier-to-noise ratio (CNR) is readily measured by first injecting an unmodulated carrier at the head-end, with a spectrum analyser measuring the signal level at the output of the last amplifier in the largest cascade of amplifiers. The carrier is then removed and, with the resolution of the spectrum analyser adjusted to match the channel bandwidth, the noise level is measured.

As an alternative to the spectrum analyser, a field strength meter may be used together with an appropriate band pass filter.

The CNR of the reverse path should also be measured by injecting the carrier at the end of the largest spur and measuring the noise level at the head-end.

The overall CNR for the system can then be calculated using the expression given in Appendix 2.

Measurement of Distortion

This test requires a signal source which can generate a number of unmodulated carriers simultaneously. These are injected at the head-end, and the level of the worse-case beat frequency at the end of the longest cascade of amplifiers is measured. As in the case of the CNR, the corresponding reverse path figure is also measured and the overall system distortion calculated (see Appendix 2).

In the absence of other standards, those applicable to cable television systems may be used. These require an overall system CNR greater than 43dB, and a distortion figure of greater than 52dB. In practice, these figures are readily achieved with broadband LANs because so few amplifiers are required, but in CATV networks noise and distortion frequently limit the size of a system.

RF Radiation Test

Noise egress from the system is important in environments where emissions may effect other services; examples of navigation and emergency radio services have already been cited, but noise can also be troublesome in less critical situations. The emissions from networks may also be limited by legislative requirements and it is good practice therefore to test networks for RF radiation levels after installation.

The highest signal levels in a system will be at the output of an amplifier, and the level of RF radiation should be measured by injecting a signal at the head-end and measuring the radiated signal strength by means of a calibrated antenna at the specified distance from the amplifier.

5 Implementing a Broadband LAN

INTRODUCTION

The process of implementing a broadband network can be described under the following major headings:

— evaluation of networking requirements;

— choosing a LAN/supplier;

— design and installation;

— operation.

EVALUATION OF NETWORKING REQUIREMENTS

As this book is primarily concerned with the implementation of a broadband LAN it is not proposed to go into detail on the mechanisms for defining a user's networking requirements.

Briefly, the requirements will revolve around the following basic issues:

— services the network is to perform;

— volume and type of network traffic;

— reliability of network;

— growth;

— maintenance;

— cost.

73

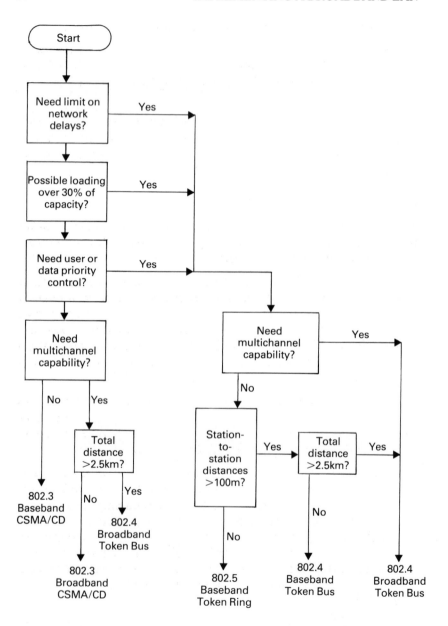

Figure 5.1

See Reference 5.1 for detailed information on this topic.

It will be assumed that the reader has carried out a thorough investigation and subsequently rejected alternative non-broadband networking solutions, eg PABX switching, data over voice multiplexing, and baseband.

Figure 5.1 shows a flowchart using criteria such as network delay, capacity, priority control, multichannel capability and distance to help network designers choose a LAN that adheres to one of the IEE 802 committee standards.

CHOOSING A LAN/SUPPLIER

Table 5.1 lists several broadband LAN products on the UK market today and, although far from being exhaustive, does represent a large slice of the systems on offer.

Broadband LANs can be divided into groups defined by their mode of operation. An example of this would be grouping by access method. If we look at Figure 5.2 we can see three major types of access: dedicated, controlled and random. These are subdivided into FDM, TDM, or SDM for dedicated access; polling or reservation for controlled access; and various types of CSMA/CD for random access methods (see Reference 5.2).

Two of the most popular access methods for broadband networks are CSMA/CD and token passing. Figure 5.3 describes briefly how these systems operate. (The section on access protocol issues in Chapter 2 deals with this subject in greater detail.)

No one access method is ideal under all circumstances. The major characteristics and applications for the different methods are shown in Figure 5.4. Here we see that token passing is suited to a small number of attached devices with large amounts of data, whereas CSMA/CD can cater for a large number of devices but with 'bursty' type traffic. On the other hand a dedicated access method such as FDM, TDM or SDM would be excellent for process control applications where a communications channel must be available at all times.

Let us look at one example of each type of access method by briefly describing a product that uses it.

Manufacturer/ Distributor	Telephone	Product Name	Description	Cable
SYFA DATA SYSTEMS	0923 771211	SYFANET	CSMA/CA	75Ω Standard
FERRANTI	061 499 3355	BROADBAND	FDM, Point-to-Point, Multidrop	CATV Coaxial
IBM (UK)	01 578 4399	PC NET (BROADBAND)	CSMA	RG11 Coaxial
INFOTRON	0305 66016	INX 4000	—	25 Twisted Pairs or Fibre
ITL	04862 28171	CABLESTREAM LOCAL NET	CSMA/CD	CATV Coaxial
LION SYSTEMS	02402 63951	INFOBUS DCA	CSMA/CD	CATV Coaxial
PHILIPS (BUSINESS SYSTEMS)	0206 575115	SOPHO-LAN	Token Passing Bus	CATV Coaxial
UNGERMANN-BASS	0628 71411	NET/ONE	CSMA	
WANG (UK)	01 560 4151	WANG BAND WANG NET	CSMA/CD	CATV Coaxial
ALAN BRADLEY (INTERNATIONAL) (formerly 3M (UK))	061 486 0722	LAN/1 LAN PC	Token Passing Bus	CATV Coaxial RG11 Coaxial

Table 5.1

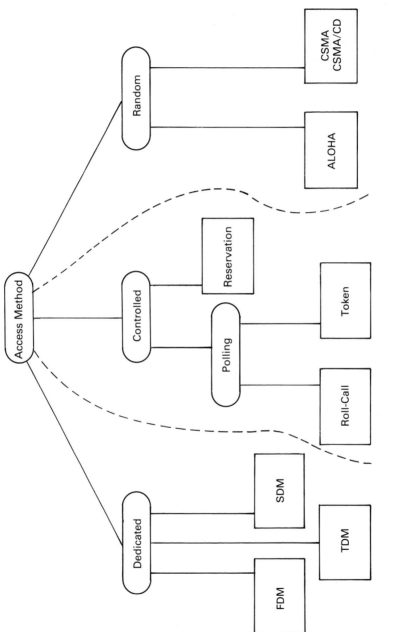

Figure 5.2

(a) Token Passing

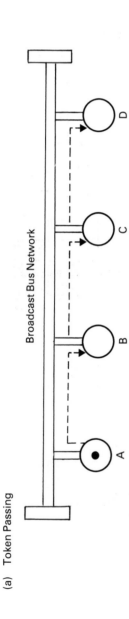

Broadcast Bus Network

If A has the token it broadcasts on the bus. Subsequently A passes the token to B.

(b) CSMA/CD

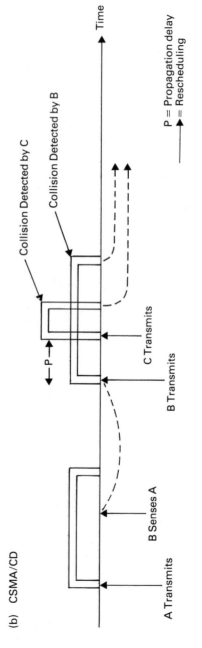

P = Propagation delay
⬆ = Rescheduling

Figure 5.3

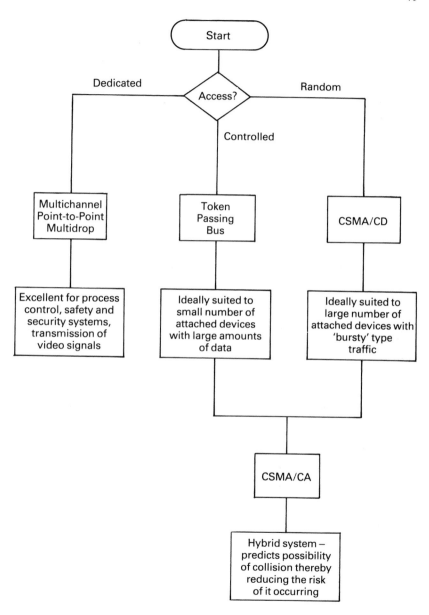

Figure 5.4

Dedicated Access – Ferranti Broadband

The Ferranti broadband network uses RF frequencies between 5 MHz and 300 MHz divided into forward and reverse channel frequency bands separated by a guard band. Each data communications link is allocated a forward and reverse frequency pair.

Point-to-point

In a point-to-point network the RF modems operate as linked pairs. The RF modem at the terminal corresponds in transmit and receive frequencies to one at the head-end (see Figure 5.5). The RF modems can operate synchronously or asynchronously and the maximum data rate is dependent on the bandwidth allocated.

Multidrop

A multidrop configuration uses a single head-end modem with separate modems for each remote site. The system operates on a single pair of frequencies to which all the modems are tuned. Each device on the network has a unique address and is polled by the host CPU for data.

Controlled Access – 3M LAN/1

The 3M LAN/1 system, although operating on a physical bus medium, functions as a logical ring using a token-passing protocol to control network traffic (see Figure 5.6).

When the Network Interfacing Unit (NIU) has traffic for the network it captures the circulating electronic token and sends data for a controlled period of time.

Access is balanced so that each port has equal access time. A message length lock-out feature prevents an individual NIU from capturing the token beyond the maximum allowable period.

The system can operate on up to five channel pairs, each pair supporting up to 2000 users via 250 NIUs. A communication speed of 2.5 Mbps is possible over a radius of seven miles from the channel converter. Individual devices can communicate at 19.2 Kbps. LAN/1 also handles video distribution and point-to-point facilities.

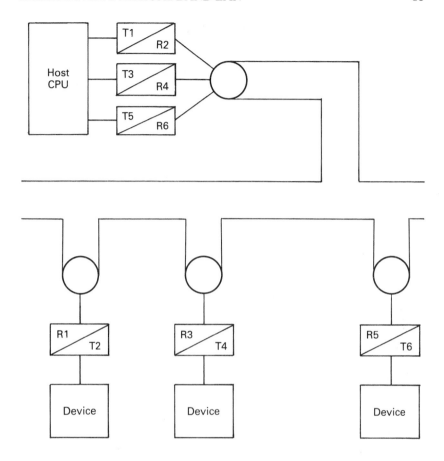

Figure 5.5   Ferranti Broadband

Random Access – ITL CableStream/Local Net 20

CableStream is a broadband system incorporating a family of developing products which consist of three principal sub-networks:

— DigiStream: data and text communications;

— ImageStream: broadcasting of television images;

— VoiceStream: telephoning.

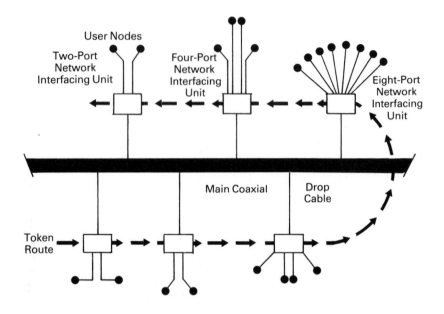

Figure 5.6   3M LAN/1

DigiStream provides transmission, switching, multiplexing, error detection, recovery and gateway access to British Telecom's KiloStream, MegaStream, Datel and packet-switched services, fibre optics, and IBM's Systems Network Architecture (SNA). DigiStream is complemented by ImageStream and VoiceStream which enhance the features offered to include video and voice transmission.

Local Net 20 is based on packet switching, CSMA/CD and FDM techniques. The channels are contained in two 36 MHz bands, between 70 and 106 MHz, for transmitting data from any packet communications unit to the broadband translator (TVERTER). This converts the entire 36 MHz low band to a high band occupying 226-262 MHz for retransmission along the cable to receive a section of each packet communications unit. Each of the 120 channels supports a 128 Kbps data rate.

Figure 5.7 describes the logical layout of a Local Net 20 system.

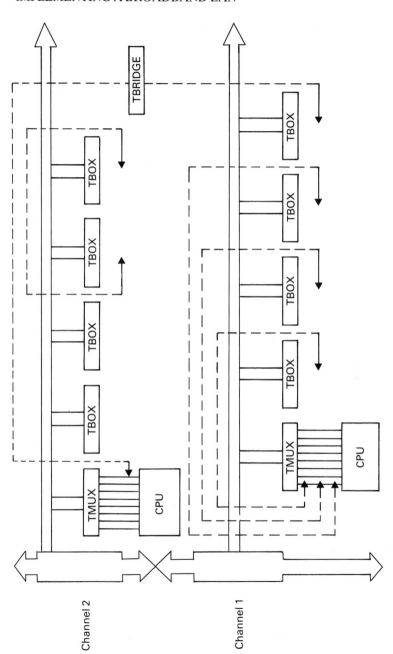

Figure 5.7   Logical Layout of Local Net 20 System

DESIGN AND INSTALLATION

Design

When designing the physical layout of a broadband LAN, issues such as the type of building, regulations in force, and the LAN configuration specifications must be taken into account.

New Buildings

This is an excellent opportunity for installing a LAN. The architect can plan for concealed ducting to accommodate the trunk and branch cables. Data ports can be provided as required into every office.

Existing Buildings

Office accommodation, warehouses and manufacturing premises vary considerably in construction.

The installation planner should survey the site thoroughly with assistance from the authorities responsible for the users' premises, eg the site service manager. Ideally this person will have intimate knowledge of the existing power sources, risers and conduits, wireways, firewalls, etc and can provide floor plans and other consultant services.

Cable Routes

Each site should be carefully evaluated by the network planners to determine the best routeing for the cable. Preferred routes are above the ceiling, taking into account unique features such as suspended ceilings, floor conduits, raised floors and inter-building requirements.

The route should take into acccount the following suggestions:

— avoid areas in which electrical noise is present (broadband has a high immunity factor inherent in its design so this should not present too many problems);

— avoid areas where mechanical damage is likely to occur;

— choose the most accessible route (this will allow the network to be extended, or damaged cable to be quickly replaced);

— choose the route least likely to be disturbed;

— choose the shortest route if at all possible (this will keep cabling costs down and there is less cable to go wrong!).

Floor Plan Layout

Once the site has been surveyed and evaluated and the best route for the cable has been chosen it is essential that a floor plan be drawn up establishing the positions of trunks, branches, amplifiers and splitters, etc. This plan should be constantly kept up-to-date.

Network Installations

Network design and installation for a broadband LAN is a complex task involving signal strength equalisation at all tap locations, care in positioning amplifiers, splitters and taps, and in calculating tap values. This requires an experienced CATV design engineer with RF engineering skills not usually present in a customer's workforce (see Note below).

Both ITL (Sytek) and Ferranti offer cable design and consultancy right through to a 'turnkey' solution if required. Typical services include:

Site survey — determine optimum cable route and design for the LAN

Layout and design — design and prepare drawings for a vendor-independent network on a standard broadband cable

System specification — includes scope of work, labour requirements, contractor obligations, component specifications and design criteria. The resultant specification enables a customer to obtain meaningful bids

System certification — ensures functional requirements of a network are met

Engineering/systems — communications applications assistance
analysis with installation, network configuration
and on-site evaluation

Training and
consultancy

> Note: Products such as the IBM PC broadband and
> SYFA Data Systems SYFANET are designed to be
> user installed by employing passive techniques (ie no
> ampliers, head-end, etc) on standard 75Ω coaxial
> cable.

OPERATION

Broadband LANs of any size will require periodic alignment and
maintenance. (Amplifiers, for instance, must be adjusted for gain
and slope.)

Network monitoring and control are of extreme importance too,
as placing all communications on a single CATV cable increases
the risk of total or partial failure. Modems and components which
degrade network performance must be quickly isolated and
replaced.

Nearly all broadband LANs have some form of network management included. The 3M LAN/1 network management is accomp-
lished with the aid of a Network Monitor Unit (NMU) which receives
and processes information on network activity. The NMU generates
statistics and maintains records of system performance. If necessary
the unit can be accessed through a telephone for remote system
diagnosis and functional analysis. (The NMU consists of an IBM
personal computer and 3M software.)

Successful operation of a broadband LAN will depend on the
effective control of operational, maintenance and management
procedures.

Operational Control

Examples of operational control, which aids managerial and
maintenance control, are:

— security and authorisation by means of password, sign-on, encryption, etc;

— parameter-driven configuration changes;

— resource control by availability analysis and use;

— activation and de-activation of resources;

— statistical information, instantaneous and cumulative;

— accounting and billing.

Maintenance Control

The purpose of good maintenance control is to provide a means of detecting, diagnosing and rectifying abnormal operation in an effort to minimise the impact on the network as a whole.

Fault minimisation	— provide back-up of critical components in the network, eg head-end and main trunk
Self-test	— provide loopback facilities on RF modems
Fault detection/ location	— detection of signal framing lost, capture of transient faults, threshold detection on unacceptable errors and detection of tapping
Fault diagnosis	— provide trace and monitoring facilities. Use of tester, trap or loop test on all network paths. Fault isolation on network components
Rectification/ recovery	— station or resource isolation, component repair or replacement and critical resource duplication

Management Control

Management control consists of:

— network characteristics by traffic, inventory, resource and service analysis;

— network growth or subtraction;

— peak/average traffic analysis;

— performance analysis, eg response times;

— error rate monitoring;

— transient error monitoring;

— security control, eg encryption;

— tuning the network;

— control of the network software.

SUMMARY

Successful operation of a broadband LAN will depend on good control. Ensure that the product you choose can supply you with the necessary hardware and software network management tools that you will require to run your network effectively.

It is unlikely that you will find all the features mentioned in this chapter available from one product. In cases where the product is right for your organisation but elements of diagnostics and statistics are missing then it may be worth considering a third party to supply the extra network management you require.

6 The Future of Broadband LANs

INTRODUCTION

The first generation of LANs solved the problem of local communications between computers and terminals but the trend for users' requirements in the areas of advanced graphics and image processing will require alternative methods of networking.

The 1980s have seen important new technical advances in:

— distributed computing;

— the user interface;

— graphics and imaging.

Distributed Computing

Future systems will have access to multiple computer resources from a single integrated workstation. This desktop device will be linked into a highly switchable network enabling the user to gain access to the many services offered by the 'information servers'.

Transparency between different types of computers and their operating systems will be a major design consideration allowing a network user to access data, programs and files from the many sources available.

The User Interface

As microprocessors become more powerful and the cost of memory continues to fall, workstations can be designed with greater friendliness and flexibility.

Extremely high resolution colour graphics will become standard features and advances in the human interface, eg touch screens and voice-operated consoles, will make it easier for the user to steer through the intricate networks of the future (see Reference 6.1).

Image Processing

Image processing enables visual patterns to be combined with data and text. As high resolution graphics have become indispensable to the business world it can be foreseen that image processing will follow in its footsteps allowing as it does photographs, still- or full-motion to be digitally encoded and processed.

BROADBAND CAN SUPPLY THE BANDWIDTH

Common to all the new technological advances mentioned is a requirement for high-speed, high-capacity communication. Broadband systems can meet these requirements, and are competing effectively with baseband technology, by offering a higher bandwidth and a greater diversity of services.

If we look at the emerging technologies within the computing world we can see how a broadband system can play a significant part in a communications network.

Artificial Intelligence

The main impetus behind artificial intelligence (AI) is provided by machines and software which are self-learning and which can effectively analyse a situation and infer from this the best course of action to take.

AI needs large quantities of raw computer power and will also require high-capacity communications channels to link AI processors. At the present time, and indeed in the foreseeable future, only broadband LANs are capable of providing this service effectively.

Optical Storage Systems

Many business organisations, eg legal and financial, have a requirement to quickly retrieve copies of an original document. To achieve the desired resolution of the document may take anything up to half a million bits of information and, in the case of two or more documents being required simultaneously, could require the transfer of several million bits of information between the optical storage terminal and its controller.

Simultaneous retrieval of data or text may also be required together with the image from the optical store. Here the multichannel working coupled with the high-capacity, high-speed characteristics of a broadband system make it an ideal choice for this type of application.

Videophones

Perhaps the most popular video services are those which offer split-screen facilities. To achieve this a two-camera system will enable simultaneous viewing of both the person speaking and any documentation relevant to the discussion in hand. This is ideally suited to the multichannel capability of a broadband system.

Other Applications

Identity cards and passwords, as used by cash dispensers, have proved to be vulnerable to fraud. Voiceprints or fingerprints could provide a new way of performing access security before the end of the decade. The high resolution required by these types of system would demand high bandwidth.

As new cable services take a hold on the community, those areas with access to the network will be able to exploit the communications facilities for new ways of working. Small broadband LANs in the home could connect to videotex, corporate computer services and a videophone through the cable network to provide the necessary tools for an employee to work from home. The system, as well as providing business links, could also provide domestic control such as home security and energy management.

FIBRE OPTICS IN BROADBAND LANS

Fibre-optic technology provides high bandwidth, light weight, noise immunity, and resistance to tapping, making it a very attractive medium for local area network implementation. Fibres can in certain cases provide up to 250 times more bandwidth than conventional coaxial cable (see Reference 6.2).

Unfortunately, fibre optics can be regarded as still being in its infancy and several design problems need to be overcome, eg tapping a signal from the fibre, connecting the fibres to other network components and finding a suitable network architecture for the physical and logical LAN design.

Broadband LANs are usually based on a bus configuration which is the most difficult type in which to implement fibre technology as so much tapping is required.

One solution to this problem has been offered in the Ungermann-Bass fibre optic Net/One LAN which physically uses a star configuration but is logically arranged as a bus.

CONCLUSION

This chapter has briefly examined a few of the recent trends in computer communications. They have in common a requirement for high-speed, high-channel-capacity links but in addition will benefit from the unique characteristics, eg multichannel working, that currently only a broadband cable system can provide.

The timescale for its universal acceptance as a networking medium may well depend on broadband systems coming down in price, which in turn will stimulate growth in the new communications services and image-based technologies.

In the final analysis there can be no doubt whatsoever that broadband systems will have an important contribution to make towards the networks of the future.

Appendix A

Principles of Broadband LANs

INTRODUCTION

The majority of broadband networking systems are based on standard CATV cable and components, although fibre-optic links are now being offered as an alternative.

Directional couplers and splitters allow the cable to be branched where required and multiport taps provide signal access points. Amplifiers restore signal strength which has been lost through the cable runs, splitters and taps.

FDM POINT-TO-POINT/MULTIDROP

Broadband LANs originated in the USA where initially the users were large industrial organisations, eg vehicle manufacturers and chemical plants, who had a requirement for increasing the transmission capacity of a single cable to keep down the costs of cabling.

As this increased capacity was the major consideration at that time, a broadband cabling system was not envisaged as the 'LAN' we are familiar with today but simply as a technique for multiplexing many channels from one cable.

Frequency Division Multiplexing (FDM) is employed to split the high bandwidth available on the CATV cable (typically 300 MHz) into a large number of individual channels. Configuration is based on either a one-cable (mid-split system) or a two-cable system.

In a two-cable system (see Figue A.1) one cable is used for transmitting information and the other for receiving information. Each

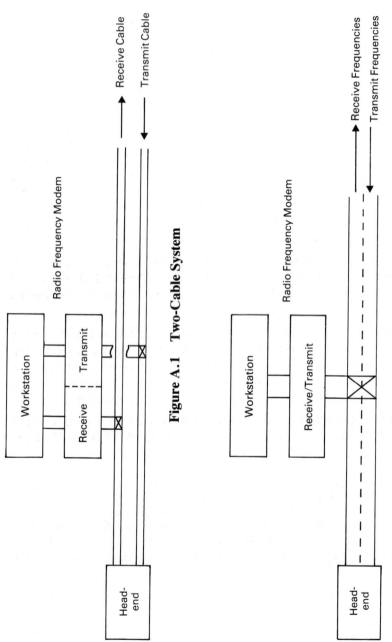

Figure A.1 Two-Cable System

Figure A.2 One-Cable System

workstation on the network is connected to both cables which run close together throughout the network until they enter the head-end. The head-end is a transmitter/receiver which listens in to all the transmissions on the transmit cable and sends them out again on the receive cable. Each workstation is interfaced to both cables via a radio frequency (RF) modem, thus creating send and receive channels for the attached device.

The one-cable system (or mid-split system), as the name implies, uses only one cable whose available bandwidth is split into two separate bands (see Figure A.2). One band is given the job of transmitting information and the other of receiving information. The single cable enters the head-end which listens to the transmissions in the transmit frequency range and passes them out on the receive frequency range.

A typical example of this FDM point-to-point operation is shown in Figure A.3. Here we see four terminals linked via four pairs of RF modems, each set to their own frequencies, connected to four ports of a host computer.

This approach, whilst having the advantage of effectively allowing one or two cables to support many channels, has the disadvantage of requiring a pair of RF modems for each device connected onto the network. Due to the relatively high cost of RF modems this can have a considerable effect on the total cost of the system.

Another problem with FDM point-to-point operation is that it prevents one device communicating with another unless they are both equipped with modems operating at the same frequency.

FDM SUPERIMPOSED WITH CSMA OR TOKEN-PASSING TECHNIQUES

Later systems now include allocating one or more pairs of channels to be used as buses, and using access protocols such as CSMA or token passing to provide a bandwidth of several million bits per second to be shared by many users.

Unallocated channels are still available for point-to-point applications, eg voice or video transmission (see Figure A.4). This type of operation provides more effective use and control of the LAN through switching and contention.

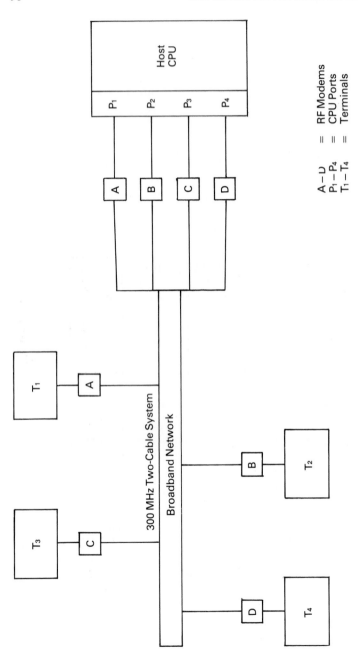

A – D   = RF Modems
$P_1 – P_4$ = CPU Ports
$T_1 – T_4$ = Terminals

Figure A.3

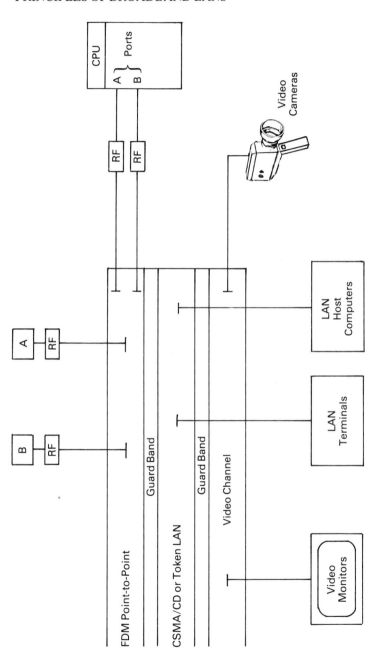

Figure A.4

Such systems offer greater potential as LANs than their FDM point-to-point predecessor, except for process control type applications where a dedicated point-to-point channel may be essential.

Appendix B

Performance of Cascaded Amplifiers

IDENTICAL AMPLIFIERS

For N cascaded amplifiers, each having a carrier-to-noise ratio CNR, the overall carrier-to-noise ratio, CNR_o, is given by:

$$CNR_o = CNR - 10 \log_{10}N$$

If each amplifier has a cross modulation D, the overall cross-modulation, D_o, is given by:

$$D_o = -D + 20 \log_{10}N$$

DISSIMILAR AMPLIFIERS

For two amplifiers (or systems) with carrier-to-noise ratios of CNR_A and CNR_B, the overall carrier-to-noise ratio is given by:

$$CNR_o = -10 \log_{10} \left[10^{\frac{-CNR_A}{10}} + 10^{\frac{-CNR_B}{10}} \right]$$

If the amplifiers (or systems) have cross-modulation figures of D_A and D_B, the overall cross-modulation figure, D_o, is given by:

$$D_o = 20 \log_{10} \left[10^{\frac{-D_A}{20}} + 10^{\frac{-D_B}{20}} \right]$$

References

CHAPTER 1

1.1 *Local Area Networks,* Kirk Gee, NCC Publications, 1982, ISBN 0 85012 365 8, pp 15-26

1.2 *Local Area Networks,* Report to the FOCUS Committee by the LAN Standardisation Project Team (Department of Industry), August 1982, pp 14-17

1.3 Flexible manufacture, *Industrial Robot,* Vol 10, No 1, March 1983

1.4 FMS – the way ahead for batch production, John Hender, *Industrial Management and Data Systems,* May/June 1984

CHAPTER 2

2.1 Local network performance, William Stallings, *IEE Communications Magazine,* Vol 22, No 2, Feb 1984

2.2 *Performance Characteristics of Token Bus Networks,* Li L, Cherukiuri R and Bergman R, Gould Inc, USA

2.3 Integrated voice and data networks, Marson M A and Albertengo G, *Computer Communications,* Vol 5, No 3, June 1982

2.4 Voice/data integration on Ethernet – back-off and priority considerations, Chlamtac I and Eisenger M, *Computer Communications,* Vol 6, No 5, Oct 1983

CHAPTER 3

3.1 *Coupling to Shielded Cables,* E F Vance, John Wiley & Sons Ltd, 1978

3.2 *Optimised and super-screened cables,* Report by Martin Green, Wire & Cable Division, Raychem Limited, July 1981

3.3 Brown University network – BRUNET, Shipp W and Webber H, *Microprocessors and Microsystems Magazine,* Vol 6, No 8, October 1982

3.4 Cable television, L T Mudd, *IEE Proc,* Vol 129, Pt A, No 7, September 1982

CHAPTER 4

4.1 Cable television, L T Mudd, *IEE Proc,* Vol 129, Pt A, No 7, September 1982

CHAPTER 5

5.1 *Guidelines for the Selection of Local Area Computer Networks,* National Bureau of Standards, Report No ICST/LANP-82-5, 1982

5.2 *Local Area Networks,* Kirk Gee, NCC Publications, 1982, ISBN 0 85012 365 8, Chapter 4 – Network Sharing Techniques

CHAPTER 6

6.1 Workstations in a LAN environment, Yalamanchili S, Malek M and Aggarwal J K, *Computer,* November 1984

6.2 Fibre-optic technology sheds light on local area networks, Lyn Haber, *Mini-Micro Systems,* November 1984

Glossary

Analogue transmission – Transmission of a continuously varying signal

Backbone – The physical element of a cable distribution system which provides the main trunk of the network.

Bandwidth – The range of frequencies – measured from the lowest to the highest – of a transmision medium

Baseband – A method of single-channel communication where transmitted digital signals occupy the entire bandwidth of the channel

Bridge – A device which provides a communication path between separate networks

Broadband – A method of multichannel communication where signals occupy only a portion of the medium's total bandwidth

Broadcast – All devices on the system are capable of receiving all signals transmitted by others

Bus – Computers normally employ what are commonly referred to as buses for communications between the separate circuits which go to make up the whole machine, ie the processor, storage,input/output parts, etc

Cable tap – An in-line cable component that permits drop cables to be connected to the main trunk and branch cables

CATV – Cable television (community antenna television). The distribution of television signals from a central point by means of cables

Collision – When two information signals attempt to use the same channel simultaneously

Contention – When more than one user attempts to use the same channel simultaneously

Database – An organised collection of information in which data is available to all systems instead of each specific application having its own individual collections

Drop cable – A flexible coaxial cable used to connect a user outlet to a cable tap

End user – A person who uses an information-processing system

Ethernet – A low-level, baseband, local area data communications network developed by Xerox, and supported by DEC and Intel among others

File server – A storage sub-system shared by multiple workstations on a LAN

Fixed frequency modem (FFM) – An interface device that transmits and receives data over a dedicated channel

Frequency-agile modem (FAM) – An interface device that transmits and receives data over a switched channel

Gateway – A computer system or exchange in one network which allows access to and from another network. Used to connect LANs employing different protocols, and to connect LANs to public data networks

Head-end – A transmitter/receiver device (transceiver) whose task is to listen to all the transmissions on the transmit cable and send them out again on the receive cable

Host – A computer system on which applications can be executed and which also provides a service to users of a computer network

IEEE – Institute of Electrical and Electronic Engineers

IEEE 802 – An IEEE standard concerned with LANs

Interface – A boundary between two devices or two pieces of software, across which the form and functions of the signals which pass through it are specified

LAN – A communications system designed to link computers and their associated terminals within a limited geographical area. Data transmission rates are normally much higher than in conventional data communications systems (typically 10 Mbps), and often share a single cable transmission medium

Logical connection – A connection in which the means of information transfer may not exist as a real physical entity for the duration of the call

MAN – A metropolitan area network. An extended LAN serving a city

Manchester encoding – A technique for sending information bit-serially in which the data and clock signals are combined

Modem – A piece of equipment which converts digital signals into analogue or varying electrical signals for transmission over normal telephone lines. The modem also performs the reverse function

Multiplexing – The use of a single physical link for two or more simultaneous separate transmissions. A multiplexer is the device which performs this function. It is not usually programmable by the user

Multipoint or multidrop – A circuit which is connected to several different destinations

Node – A point where one or more devices connect to the network. Nodes include minicomputers and workstations

Packet – A group of binary digits that includes data control signals and error control information. The digits are arranged in a specific format and transferred as a composite whole

Packet switching – A mode of transmission in which messages are broken into smaller increments called packets, each of which is routed independently to the destination. The network routes and transfers data by means of addressed packets, whereby a channel is occupied only during the transmission of the packet. The channel is then available for the transfer of other packets

Physical connection – A transmission means between two or more users which usually consists of electrical conductors along which signals are transmitted.

Polling – A process whereby terminals are invited one at a time to transmit information

Public data network – A communications system which is intended for transmission of digital data and which is available for anyone who wishes to subscribe to it

Repeater – A device used to regenerate, amplify and retransmit signals

Switching – In computer or communications networks, switching is the process by which services or data are directed to the appropriate user

Topology – Description of the physical connection of a specific network's nodes

Transceiver – A transmitter/receiver through which devices can access the network

WAN – A wide area network is designed to service an area of hundreds or thousands of miles. Compare with LANs and MANs

X25 – The CCITT standard defining the interface between packet type data terminal equipment and a public data network

Index